The
Modern Power Supply
and
Battery Charger Circuit
Encyclopedia

Other Books in the Series

The
Modern Power Supply
and
Battery Charger Circuit
Encyclopedia

Rudolf F. Graf

TAB BOOKS
Blue Ridge Summit, PA

FIRST EDITION
FIRST PRINTING

© 1992 by **Rudolf F. Graf**.
Published by TAB Books.
TAB Books is a division of McGraw-Hill, Inc.

Library of Congress Cataloging-in-Publication Data

Graf, Rudolf F.
    The modern power supply and battery charger circuit encyclopedia /
    by Rudolf F. Graf.
        p.   cm.
    Includes index.
    ISBN 0-8306-3923-3 (p)
    1. Battery chargers. 2. Power supply, Electric. I. Title.
TK2943.G73   1992
621.31'242—dc20   91-33708
                                                             CIP

TAB Books offers software for sale. For information and a catalog, please contact
TAB Software Department, Blue Ridge Summit, PA 17294-0850.

Acquisitions Editor: Roland S. Phelps
Book Editor: Andrew Yoder
Director of Production: Katherine G. Brown
Cover Design: Graphics Plus, Hanover, PA.   TAB1

For Daniel,
You brighten my day.
With love from Popsi

Contents

Introduction

Like the other volumes in this series, this book contains a wealth of ready-to-use circuits that serve the needs of the engineer, technician, student and, of course, the browser. These unique books contain more practical, ready-to-use circuits focused on a specific field of interest, than can be found anywhere in a single volume.

1

Battery Chargers and Zappers

The sources of the following circuits are contained in the Sources section, which begins on page 125. The figure number in the box of each circuit correlates to the source entry in the Sources section.

Lead-Acid Battery Charger
12-V Battery Charger
200-mA-hour 12-V NiCad Battery Charger
NiCad Charger with Current and Voltage Limiting
14-V 4-A Battery Charger/Power Supply
Fast Charger for NiCad Batteries
Current-Limited 6-V Charger
NiCad Charger
Simple NiCad Battery Zapper
Battery Charger
Automatic Shutoff Battery Charger
Battery-Charging Regulator
12-V Battery-Charger Control (20 rms Max.)
Battery Charger
Universal Battery Charger
Lead-Acid Low-Battery Detector

Universal Battery Charger
UJT Battery Charger
Automotive Charger for NiCad Battery Packs
Constant-Voltage Current-Limited Charger
Versatile Battery Charger
Gel-Cell Charger
NiCad Battery Zapper
PUT Battery Charger
Thermally Controlled NiCad Charger
NiCad Battery Zapper II
Portable NiCad Battery Charger
Lithium Battery Charger
Rapid Battery Charger for Icom IC-2A
Battery Charger Operates on Single Solar Cell
Wind-Powered Battery Charger

LEAD-ACID BATTERY CHARGER

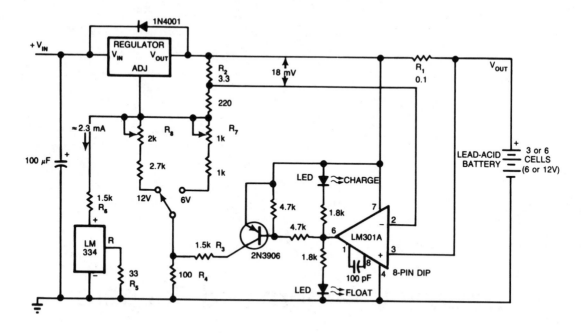

EDN

Fig. 1-1

This circuit furnishes an initial voltage of 2.5 V per cell at 25°C to rapidly charge a battery. The charging current decreases as the battery charges, and when the current drops to 180 mA, the charging circuit reduces the output voltage to 2.35 V per cell, leaving the battery in a fully charged state. This lower voltage prevents the battery from overcharging, which would shorten its life.

The LM301A compares the voltage drop across R1 with an 18 mV reference set by R2. The comparator's output controls the voltage regulator, forcing it to produce the lower float voltage when the battery-charging current, passing through R1, drops below 180 mA. The 150 mV difference between the charge and float voltages is set by the ratio of R3 to R4. The LEDs show the state of the circuit.

Temperature compensation helps prevent overcharging, particularly when a battery undergoes wide temperature changes while being charged. The LM334 temperature sensor should be placed near or on the battery to decrease the charging voltage by 4 mV/°C for each cell. Because batteries need more temperature compensation at lower temperatures, change R5 to 30 Ω for a tc of − 5 mV/°C per cell if application will see temperatures below − 20°C.

The charger's input voltage must be filtered dc that is at least 3 V higher than the maximum required output voltage: approximately 2.5 V per cell. Choose a regulator for the maximum current needed: LM371 for 2 A, LM350 for 4 A, or LM338 for 8 A. At 25°C and with no output load, adjust R7 for a V_{OUT} of 7.05 V, and adjust R8 for a V_{OUT} of 14.1 V.

12-V BATTERY CHARGER

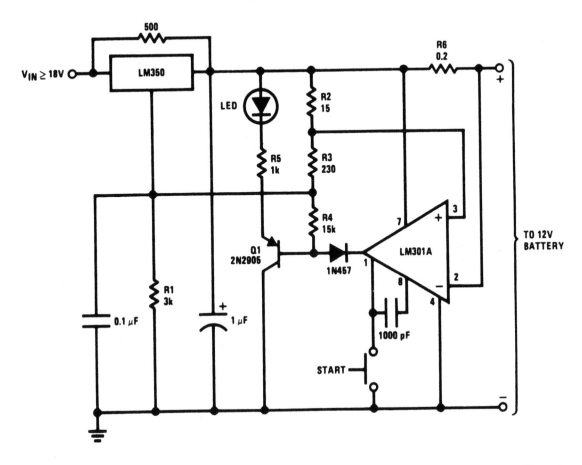

NATIONAL SEMICONDUCTOR

Fig. 1-2

This circuit is a high-performance charger for gelled-electrolyte lead-acid batteries. This charger quickly recharges the battery and shuts off at full charge. Initially, charging current is limited to 2 A. As the battery voltage rises, current to the battery decreases, and when the current has decreased to 150 mA, the charger switches to a lower float voltage, which prevents overcharge. When the start switch is pushed, the output of the charger goes to 14.5 V. As the battery approaches full charge, the charging current decreases and the output voltage is reduced from 14.5 V to about 12.5 V, terminating the charging. Transistor Q1 then lights the LED as a visual indication of full charge.

200-mA/HOUR, 12-V NICAD BATTERY CHARGER

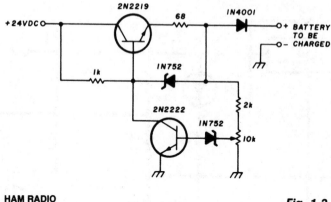

HAM RADIO

Fig. 1-3

This circuit charges the battery at 75 mA until the battery is charged, then it reduces the current to a trickle rate. It will completely recharge a dead battery in four hours and the battery can be left in the charger indefinitely. To set the shut-off point, connect a 270-Ω, 2-W resistor across the charge terminals and adjust the pot for 15.5 V across the resistor.

NICAD CHARGER WITH CURRENT AND VOLTAGE LIMITING

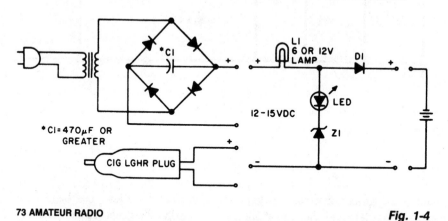

73 AMATEUR RADIO

Fig. 1-4

Lamp L1 will glow brightly and the LED will be out when the battery is low and being charged, but the LED will be bright and the light dim when the battery is almost ready. L1 should be a bulb that is rated for the current you want (usually the battery capacity divided by 10). Diode D1 should be at least 1 A, and Z1 is a 1-W zener diode with a voltage determined by the full-charge battery voltage minus 1.5 V. After the battery is fully charged, the circuit will float it at about battery capacity divided by 100 mA.

14-V 4-A BATTERY CHARGER/POWER SUPPLY

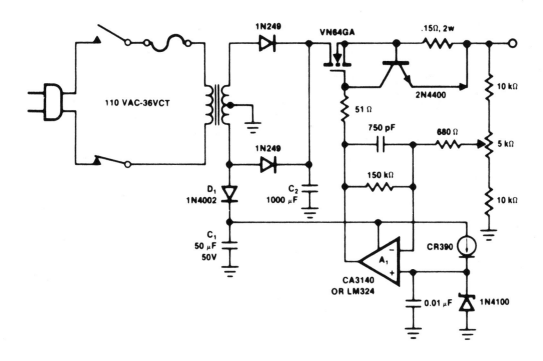

SILICONIX

Fig. 1-5

Operational amplifier A1 directly drives the VN64GA with the error signal to control the output voltage. Peak rectifier D1, C1 supplies error amplifier A1 and the reference zener. This extra drive voltage must exceed its source voltage by several volts for the VN64GA to pass full load current. The output voltage is pulsating dc, which is quite satisfactory for battery charging. To convert the system to a regulated dc supply, capacitor C2 is increased and another electrolytic capacitor is added across the load. The response time is very fast, determined by the op amp. The 2N4400 current-limiter circuit prevents the output current from exceeding 4.5 A. However, maintaining a shorted condition for more than one second will cause the VN64GA to exceed its temperature ratings. A generous heatsink, on the order of 1°C/W, must be used.

FAST CHARGER FOR NICAD BATTERIES

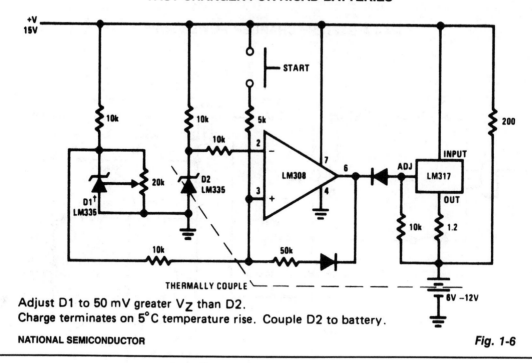

Adjust D1 to 50 mV greater V_Z than D2.
Charge terminates on 5°C temperature rise. Couple D2 to battery.

NATIONAL SEMICONDUCTOR

Fig. 1-6

CURRENT-LIMITED 6-V CHARGER

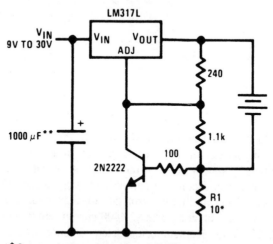

* Sets peak current, $I_{PEAK} = 0.6V/R1$

* * 1000 μF is recommended to filter out any input transients.

NATIONAL SEMICONDUCTOR

Fig. 1-7

NICAD CHARGER

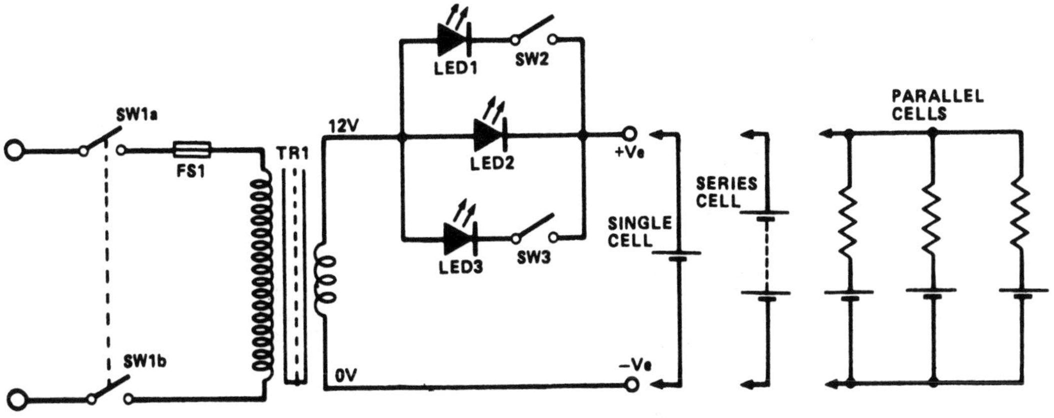

ELECTRONICS TODAY INTERNATIONAL

Fig. 1-8

This circuit uses constant current LEDs to adjust charging current. It uses LEDs that pass a constant current of about 15 mA for an applied voltage range of 2 to 18 V. They can be paralleled to give any multiple of 15 mA and they light up when current is flowing. The circuit will charge a single cell at 15, 30, or 45 mA, or cells in series up to the rated supply voltage limit (about 14 V).

SIMPLE NICAD BATTERY ZAPPER

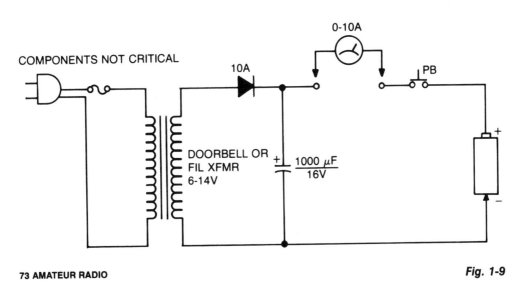

73 AMATEUR RADIO

Fig. 1-9

This circuit is used to clear internal shorts in nickel-cadmium batteries. To operate, connect a NiCad battery to the output and press the pushbutton for three seconds.

BATTERY CHARGER

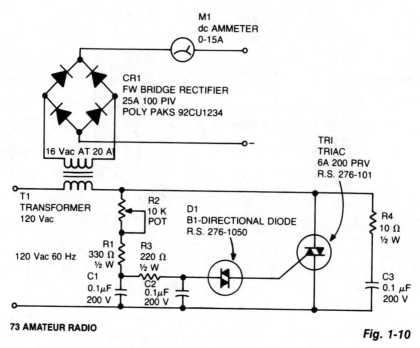

Fig. 1-10

A diac is used in the gate circuit to provide a threshold level for firing the triac. C3 and R4 provide a transient suppression network. R1, R2, R3, C1, and C2 provide a phase-shift network for the signal being applied to the gate. R1 is selected to limit the maximum charging current at full rotation of R2.

AUTOMATIC SHUTOFF BATTERY CHARGER

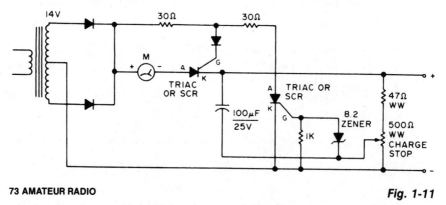

Fig. 1-11

Adjust this circuit by setting the 500-Ω resistor while it is attached to a fully charged battery.

BATTERY-CHARGING REGULATOR

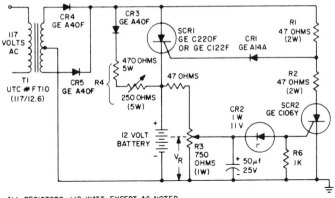

ALL RESISTORS 1/2 WATT EXCEPT AS NOTED

GE

Fig. 1-12

The circuit is capable of charging a 12-V battery at up to a six ampere rate. Other voltages and currents, from 6 to 600 V and up to 300 A, can be accommodated by suitable component selection. When the battery voltage reaches its fully charged level, the charging SCR shuts off, and a trickle charge, as determined by the value of R4, continues to flow.

12-V BATTERY-CHARGER CONTROL (20 A rms MAX.)

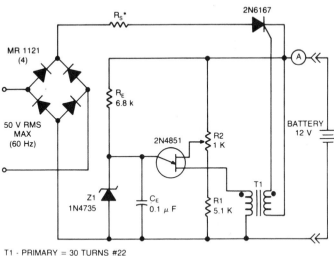

T1 - PRIMARY = 30 TURNS #22
SECONDARY = 45 TURNS #22
CORE = FERROXCUBE 203 F 181-3C3
R_S - SERIES RESISTANCE TO LIMIT CURRENT THROUGH SCR
2N6167 IS RATED AT 20 AMPS RMS.

MOTOROLA

Fig. 1-13

BATTERY CHARGER

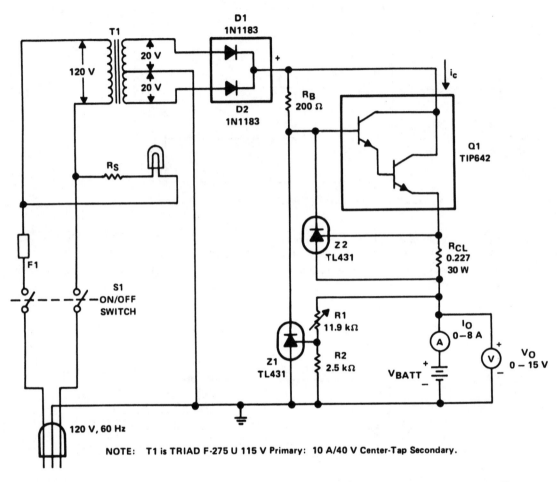

NOTE: T1 is TRIAD F-275 U 115 V Primary: 10 A/40 V Center-Tap Secondary.

TEXAS INSTRUMENTS

Fig. 1-14

    The charger is based on a charging voltage of 2.4 V per cell, in accordance with most manufacturers' recommendations. The circuit pulses the battery under charge with 14.4 V (6 cells $\times$ 2.4 V per cell) at a rate of 120 Hz. The design provides current limiting to protect the charger's internal components while limiting the charging rate to prevent damaging severely discharged lead-acid batteries. The maximum recommended charging current is normally about one-fourth the ampere-hour rating of the battery. For example, the maximum charging current for an average 44 ampere-hour battery is 11 A. If the impedance of the load requires a charging current greater than the 11 A current limit, the circuit will go into current limiting. The amplitude of the charging pulses is controlled to maintain a maximum peak charging current of 11 A (8 A average).

UNIVERSAL BATTERY CHARGER

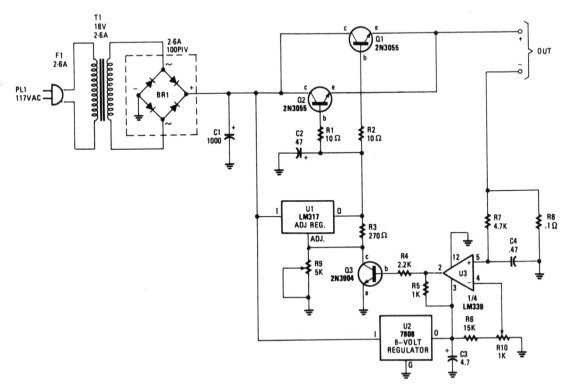

POPULAR ELECTRONICS

Fig. 1-15

The charger's output voltage is adjustable and regulated, and has an adjustable constant-current charging circuit that makes it easy to use with most NiCad batteries. The charger can charge a single cell or a number of series-connected cells up to a maximum of 18 V.

Power transistors Q1 and Q2 are connected as series regulators to control the battery charger's output voltage and charge-current rate. An LM317 adjustable voltage regulator supplies the drive signal to the bases of power transistors Q1 and Q2. Potentiometer R9 sets the output-voltage level. A current-sampling resistor, R8 (a 0.1-Ω, 5-W unit), is connected between the negative output lead and circuit ground. For each amp of charging current that flows through R8, a 100 mV output is developed across it. The voltage developed across R8 is fed to one input of comparator U3. The other input of the comparator is connected to variable resistor R10.

As the charging voltage across the battery begins to drop, the current through R8 decreases. Then the voltage feeding pin 5 of U3 decreases, and the comparator output follows, turning Q3 back off, which completes the signal's circular path to regulate the battery's charging current.

The charging current can be set by adjusting R10 for the desired current. The circuit's output voltage is set by R9.

11

LEAD-ACID LOW-BATTERY DETECTOR

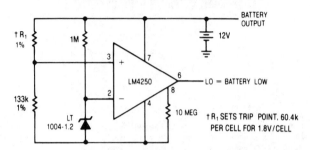

Fig. 1-16

UNIVERSAL BATTERY CHARGER

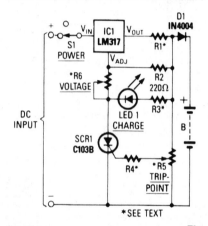

Fig. 1-17

When power is applied to the circuit, SCR1 is off, so there is no bias-current path to ground; thus, LM317 acts as a current regulator. The LM317 is connected to the battery through steering diode D1, limiting resistor R1, and bias resistor R2. The steering diode prevents the battery from discharging through the LED and the SCR when power is removed from the circuit. As the battery charges, the voltage across trip-point potentiometer R5 rises, and at some point, turns on the SCR. Then, current from the regulator can flow to ground, so the regulator now functions in the voltage mode. When the SCR turns on, it also provides LED1 with a path to ground through R3. So, when LED1 is on, the circuit is in the voltage-regulating mode; when LED1 is off, the circuit is in the current-regulating mode.

UJT BATTERY CHARGER

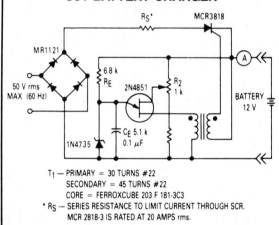

T_1 — PRIMARY = 30 TURNS #22
SECONDARY = 45 TURNS #22
CORE = FERROXCUBE 203 F 181-3C3
* R_S — SERIES RESISTANCE TO LIMIT CURRENT THROUGH SCR.
MCR 2818-3 IS RATED AT 20 AMPS rms.

Fig. 1-18

This circuit will not work unless the battery to be charged is connected with proper polarity. The battery voltage controls the charger and when the battery is fully charged, the charger will not supply current to the battery. The battery charging current is obtained through the SCR when it is triggered into the conducting state by the UJT relaxation oscillator. The oscillator is only activated when the battery voltage is low. $V_{B_2B_1}$ of the UJT is derived from the voltage of the battery to be charged, and since $V_P = V_D = V_{B_2B_1}$; the higher $V_{B_2B_1}$, the higher V_P. When V_P exceeds the breakdown voltage of the zener diode Z1, the UJT will cease to fire and the SCR will not conduct. This indicates that the battery has attained its desired charge as set by R2.

AUTOMOTIVE CHARGER FOR NICAD BATTERY PACKS

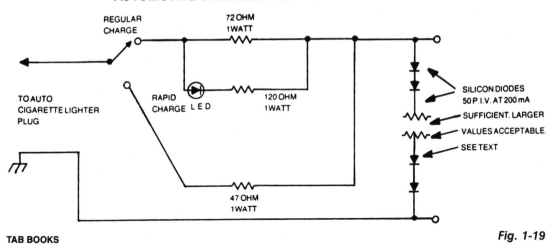

TAB BOOKS

Fig. 1-19

The number of silicon diodes across the output is determined by the voltage of the battery pack. Figure each diode at 0.7 V. For example, a 10.9-V pack would require 10.9/0.7 = 15.57, or 16 diodes.

CONSTANT-VOLTAGE CURRENT-LIMITED CHARGER

IC LM723C VOLTAGE REGULATOR (FOR 12V dc
OUTPUT 0.42A MAX.)

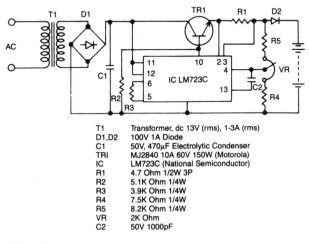

For 12-V sealed lead-acid batteries.

T1	Transformer, dc 13V (rms), 1-3A (rms)
D1,D2	100V 1A Diode
C1	50V, 470μF Electrolytic Condenser
TRI	MJ2840 10A 60V 150W (Motorola)
IC	LM723C (National Semiconductor)
R1	4.7 Ohm 1/2W 3P
R2	5.1K Ohm 1/4W
R3	3.9K Ohm 1/4W
R4	7.5K Ohm 1/4W
R5	8.2K Ohm 1/4W
VR	2K Ohm
C2	50V 1000pF

YUASA BATTERY

Fig. 1-20

VERSATILE BATTERY CHARGER

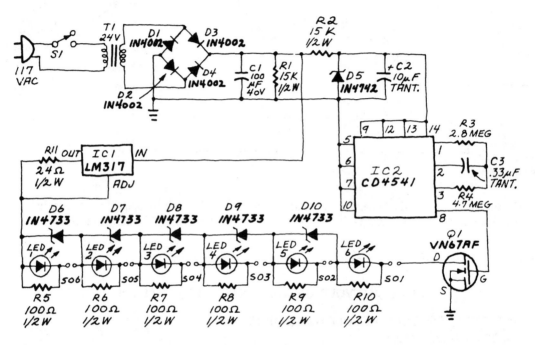

Fig. 1-21

An LM317 voltage regulator is configured as a constant-current source. It is used to supply the 50-mA charging current to S01-S06, an array of AA-cell battery holders. Each of the battery holders is wired in series with an LED and its associated shunt resistor. When the battery holder contains a battery, the LED glows during charging. Each battery holder/LED combination is paralleled by a 5.1-V zener diode. If the battery holder is empty, the zener conducts the current around the holder.

A timing circuit prevents overcharging. When power is applied to the circuit, timing is initiated by IC2, a CD4541 oscillator/programmable timer. The output of IC2 is fed to Q1. When that output is high, the transistor is on, and the charging circuit is completed. When the output is low, the transistor is off, and the path to ground is interrupted.

GEL-CELL CHARGER

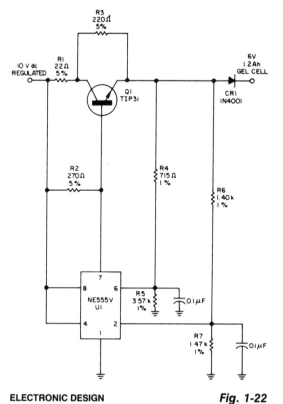

This circuit detects a full-charge state and automatically switches to a float condition—from 240 to 12 mA.

ELECTRONIC DESIGN

Fig. 1-22

NICAD BATTERY ZAPPER

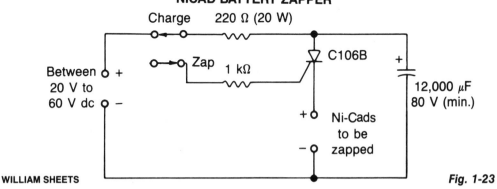

WILLIAM SHEETS

Fig. 1-23

The short in a NiCad battery can be ''burned off'' with this zapper. Use of the SCR keeps heavy discharge current from damaging switch contacts.

THERMALLY CONTROLLED NICAD CHARGER

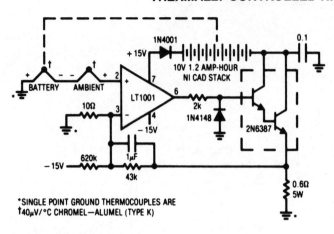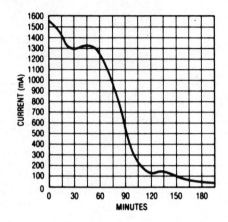

LINEAR TECHNOLOGY CORP.

Fig. 1-24

One way to charge NiCad batteries rapidly without abuse is to measure cell temperature and taper the charge accordingly. The circuit uses a thermocouple for this function. A second thermocouple nulls out the effects of ambient temperature. The temperature difference between the two thermocouples determines the voltage, which appears at the amplifier's positive input. As battery temperature rises, this small negative voltage (1°C difference between the thermocouples equals 40 μV) becomes larger. The amplifier, operating at a gain of 4300, gradually reduces the current through the battery to maintain its inputs at balance. The battery charges at a high rate until heating occurs and the circuit then tapers the charge. The values given in the circuit limit the battery-surface temperature rise over ambient to about 5°C.

NICAD BATTERY ZAPPER II

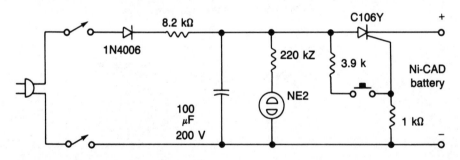

WILLIAM SHEETS

Fig. 1-25

This zapper clears internal shorts in nickel-cadmium batteries by burning them away. CAUTION: The negative battery terminal is connected to one side of the ac line. For safe operation, use a 1:1 isolation transformer.

PUT BATTERY CHARGER

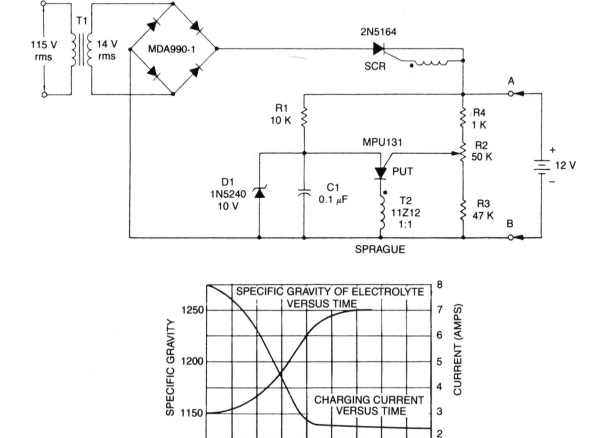

MOTOROLA

Fig. 1-26

A short-circuit-proof battery charger will provide an average charging current of about 8 A to a 12-V lead/acid storage battery. The charger circuit has an additional advantage; it will not function nor will it be damaged by improperly connecting the battery to the circuit. With 115 V at the input, the circuit commences to function when the battery is properly attached. The battery provides the current to charge the timing capacitor C1 used in the PUT relaxation oscillator. When C1 charges to the peak point voltage of the PUT, the PUT fires turning the SCR on, which in turn applies charging current to the battery. As the battery charges, the battery voltage increases slightly which increases the peak point voltage of the PUT. This means that C1 has to charge to a slightly higher voltage to fire the PUT. The voltage on C1 increases until the zener voltage of D1 is reached, which clamps the voltage on C1, and thus prevents the PUT oscillator from oscillating and charging ceases. The maximum battery voltage is set by potentiometer R2 which sets the peak point firing voltage of the PUT. In the circuit shown, the charging voltage can be set from 10 V to 14 V—the lower limit being set by D1 and the upper limit by T1.

PORTABLE NICAD BATTERY CHARGER

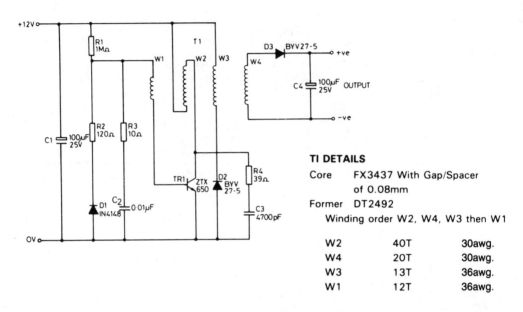

TI DETAILS

| Core | FX3437 With Gap/Spacer of 0.08mm |
| Former | DT2492 |

Winding order W2, W4, W3 then W1

W2	40T	30awg.
W4	20T	30awg.
W3	13T	36awg.
W1	12T	36awg.

ZETEX (formerly FERRANTI)

Fig. 1-27

This circuit was designed to charge NiCad battery packs in the range of 4.8 to 15.6 V from a convenient remote power source, such as an automobile battery. When power is first applied to the circuit, a small bias current supplied by R1 via winding W1, starts to turn on the transistor TR1. This forces a voltage across W2 and the positive feedback given by the coupling of W1 and W2 causes the transistor to turn hard on, applying the full supply across W2. The base drive voltage induced across W1 makes the junction between R1 and R2 become negative with respect to the 0-V supply, forward-biasing diode D1 to provide the necessary base current to hold TR1 on.

With the transistor on, a magnetizing current builds up in W2, which eventually saturates the ferrite core of transformer T1. This results in a sudden increase on the collector current flowing through TR1, causing its collector-emitter voltage to rise, and thus reducing the voltage across W2. The current flowing in W2 forces the collector voltage of the TR1 to swing positive until restricted by transformer output loading. Rc network R4 and C3 limits the turn off transient TR1. R3 and C2 maintain the loop gain of the circuit when diode D1 is not conducting.

LITHIUM BATTERY CHARGER

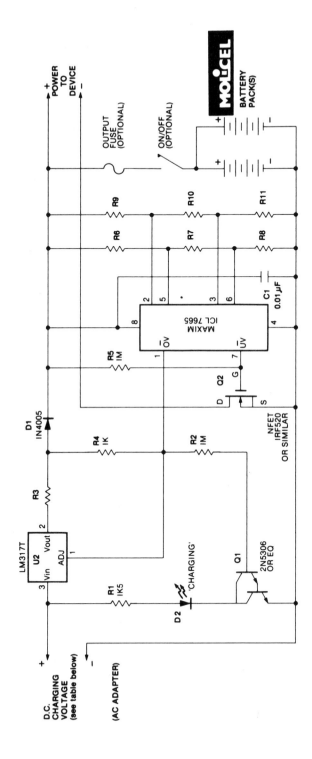

MOLI ENERGY LIMITED

Fig. 1-28

Charging is accomplished with a constant current of 60 mA for AA cells to a cutoff voltage of 2.4 V per cell, at which point the charge must be terminated. The charging system shown is designed for multi-cell battery packs of 2 to 6 series-connected cells or series/parallel arrangements. It is essential that all cells assembled in the pack are at an identical state-of-charge (voltage) before charging. The maximum upper cut-off voltage is 15.6 V (6×2.6 V).

RAPID BATTERY CHARGER FOR ICOM IC-2A

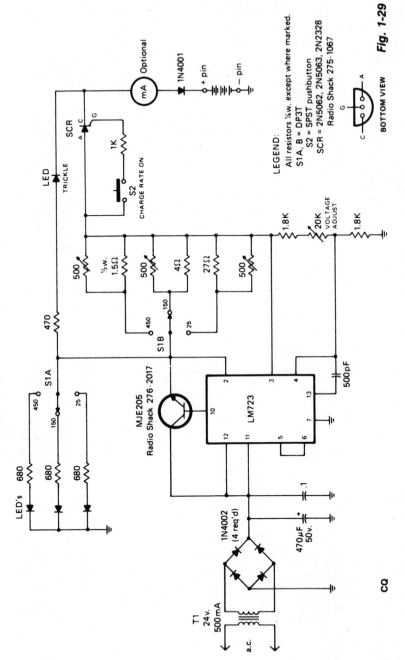

LEGEND:
All resistors ¼w. except where marked.
S1A, B = DP3T
S2 = SPST pushbutton
SCR = 2N5062, 2N5063, 2N2328
Radio Shack 275-1067

Fig. 1-29

Rectified and filtered voltage from the 24-Vac transformer is applied to the LM723 voltage regulator and the npn pass transistor set up for constant current supply. The 470-Ω resistor limits trickle current until the momentary pushbutton (S2) is depressed, the SCR turns on, and current flows through the previously determined resistor network, which limits the charging current. The SCR will turn off when the thermal cutout circuit inside the battery pack opens up.

BATTERY CHARGER OPERATES ON SINGLE SOLAR CELL

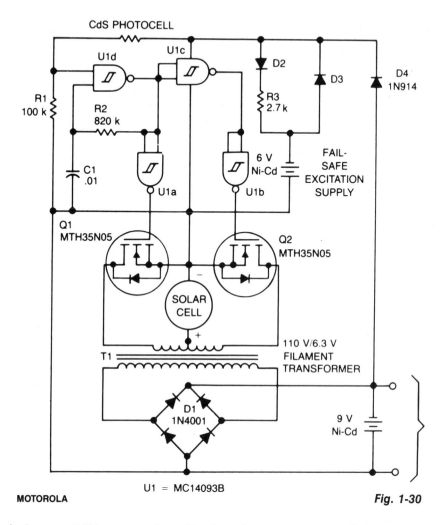

U1 = MC14093B

Fig. 1-30

The circuit charges a 9-V battery at about 30 mA per input ampere at 0.4 V. U1, a quad Schmitt trigger, operates as an astable multivibrator to drive push-pull TMOS devices, Q1 and Q2. Power for U1 is derived from the 9-V battery via D4; power for Q1 and Q2 is supplied by the solar cell. The multivibrator frequency, determined by R2/C1, is set to 180 Hz for maximum efficiency from a 6.3-V filament transformer, T1. The secondary of the transformer is applied to a full-wave bridge rectifier, D1, which is connected to the batteries being charged. The small NiCad battery is a fail-safe excitation supply to allow the system to recover if the 9-V battery becomes fully discharged.

A CdS photocell shuts off the oscillator in darkness to preserve the fail-safe battery during shipping, storage, and prolonged darkness.

WIND-POWERED BATTERY CHARGER

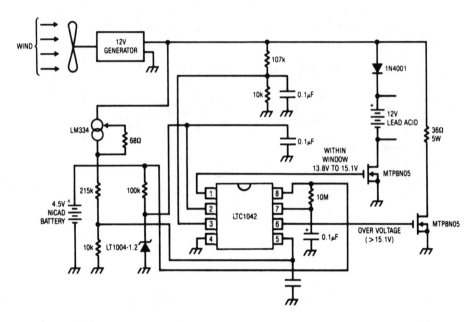

LINEAR TECHNOLOGY

Fig. 1-31

The dc motor is used as a generator; the voltage output is proportional to its rpm. The LTC1042 monitors the voltage output and provides the following control functions.

1. If generator voltage output is below 13.8 V, the control circuit is active and the NiCad battery is charging through the LM334 current source. The lead-acid battery is not being charged.
2. If the generator voltage output is between 13.8 and 15.1 V, the 12-V lead-acid battery is being charged at about 1-amp/hour rate (limited by the power FET).
3. If generator voltage exceeds 15.1 V (a condition caused by excessive wind speed or when the 12-V battery is fully charged), then a fixed load is connected, which limits the generator rpm to prevent damage.

This charger can be used as a remote source of power where wind energy is plentiful, such as on sailboats or at remote radio repeater sites. Unlike solar-powered panels, this system will function in bad weather and at night.

2

Power Supplies—Fixed

The sources of the following circuits are contained in the Sources section, which begins on page 125. The figure number in the box of each circuit correlates to the source entry in the Sources section.

General-Purpose Power Supply
12-Vdc Battery-Operated 120-Vac Power Source
Simple Power Supply
Charge-Pool Power Supply
Bilateral Current Source
3- to 30-V Universal Power-Supply Module
Regulator/Current Source
Low-Power Switching Regulator
Variable Voltage Regulator
Switching Power Supply
100-kHz Multiple-Output Switching Power Supply
Isolated Feedback Power Supply
Dual-Tracking Regulator
+15-V 1-A Regulated Power Supply
−15-V 1-A Regulated Power Supply
Hand-Held Transceiver dc Adapter
Low-Dropout 5-V Regulator
Triac-Controlled Voltage Doubler
High-Stability 10-V Regulator
Voltage-Controlled Current Source

Low-Power Inverter
Three-Rail Power Supply
Programmable Power Supply
Efficient Negative Voltage Regulator
5 V-to-Isolated 5 V (at 20 mA) Converter
Positive Regulator with npn and pnp Boost
Tracking Preregulator
Adjustable 10-A Regulator
Low-Cost Low-Dropout Linear Regulator
Voltage Doubler
Safe Constant-Current Source
Low-Cost 3-A Switching Regulator
50-W Off-Line Switching Power Supply
Positive Regulator with pnp Boost
Low Forward-Drop Rectifier Circuit
Low-Ripple Power Supply
5.0-V/10-A Regulator
5.0-V/3.0-A Regulator
Bench-Top Power Supply
Variable Current Source (100 mA to 2 A)

GENERAL-PURPOSE POWER SUPPLY

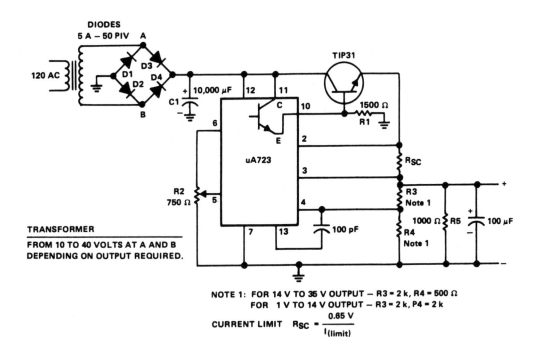

NOTE 1: FOR 14 V TO 35 V OUTPUT — R3 = 2 k, R4 = 500 Ω
FOR 1 V TO 14 V OUTPUT — R3 = 2 k, P4 = 2 k

$$\text{CURRENT LIMIT} \quad R_{SC} = \frac{0.65 \text{ V}}{I_{(limit)}}$$

TEXAS INSTRUMENTS

Fig. 2-1

The supply can be used for supply output voltages from 1 to 35 V. The line transformer should be selected to give about 1.4 times the desired output voltage from the positive side of filter capacitor C1 to ground. Potentiometer R2 sets the output voltage to the desired value by adjusting the reference input. R_{SC} is the current limit set resistor. Its value is calculated as:

$$R_{SC} = \frac{0.65 \text{ V}}{I_L}$$

For example, if the maximum current output is to be 1 A, $R_{SC} = 0.65/1.0 = 0.65$ Ω. The 1-kΩ resistor, R_S, is a light-loaded resistor designed to improve the no-load stability of the supply.

12-Vdc BATTERY-OPERATED 120-Vac POWER SOURCE

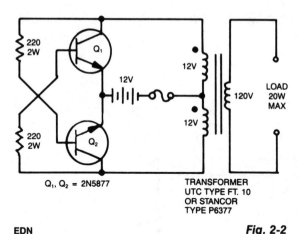

Q₁, Q₂ = 2N5877

TRANSFORMER
UTC TYPE FT. 10
OR STANCOR
TYPE P6377

EDN

Fig. 2-2

If Q1 is faster and has a higher gain than Q2, it will turn on first when you apply the input power and will hold Q2 off. Load current and transformer magnetizing current then flows in the upper half of the primary winding, and auto transformer action supplies the base drive until the transformer saturates. When that action occurs, Q1 loses its base drive. As it turns off, the transformer voltages reverse, turning Q2 on and repeating the cycle. The output frequency depends on the transformer iron and input voltage, but not on the load. The frequency will generally range between 50 to 60 Hz with a 60-Hz transformer and car battery or equivalent source. The output voltage depends on turns ratio and the difference between input voltage and transistor saturation voltage. For higher power, use larger transformers and transistors. This type of inverter normally is used in radios, phonographs, hand tools, shavers, and small fluorescent lamps. It will not work with reactive loads (motors) or loads with high inrush currents, such as coffee pots, frying pans, and heaters.

A simple 120 V: 24 V, center-tapped control transformer and four additional components can do the job. This circuit outputs a clean 200-V pk-pk square wave at 60 Hz and can supply up to 20 W. The circuit is self-starting and free-running.

SIMPLE POWER SUPPLY

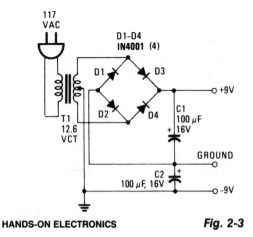

HANDS-ON ELECTRONICS

Fig. 2-3

This power supply delivers plus and minus 9 V to replace two 9-V batteries. The rectifier circuit is actually two separate full-wave rectifiers fed from the secondary of the transformer. One full-wave rectifier is composed of diodes D1 and D2, which develop +9 V, and the other is composed of D3 and D4, which develop −9 V.

Each diode from every pair rectifies 6.3 Vac, half the secondary voltage, and charges the associated filter capacitor to the peak value of the ac waveform, $6.3 \times 1.414 = 8.9$ V. Each diode should have a PIV, Peak Inverse Voltage, rating that is at least twice the peak voltage from the transformer, $2 \times 8.9 = 18$ V. The 1N4001 has a PIV of 50 V.

CHARGE-POOL POWER SUPPLY

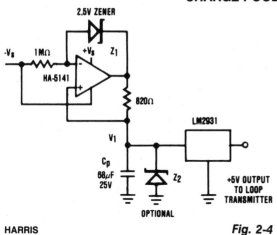

2.5V ZENER

$-V_s$ 1MΩ +V_s Z_1

HA-5141

820Ω

LM2931

V_1

C_p
68μF
25V

Z_2 OPTIONAL

+5V OUTPUT
TO LOOP
TRANSMITTER

HARRIS

Fig. 2-4

It is usually desirable to have the remote transmitter of a 4- to 20-mA current loop system powered directly from the transmission line. In some cases, this is not possible because of the high-power requirements set by the remote sensor/transmitter system. In these cases, an alternative to the separate power supply is still possible. If the remote transmitter can be operated in a pulsed mode where it is active only long enough to perform its function, then a charge pool power supply can still allow the transmitter to be powered directly by the current loop. In this circuit, constant current I_1 is supplied to the charge pool capacitor, CP, by the HA-5141 (where $I_1 = 3$ mA). The voltage V_1 continues to rise until the output of the HA-5141 approaches $+V_s$ or the optional voltage limiting provided by Z2. The LM2931 voltage regulator supplies the transmitter with a stable $+5$-V supply from the charge collected by CP. Available power supply current is determined by the duration, allowable voltage drop on CP, and required repetition rate. For example, if V_1 is allowed to drop 4.4 V and the duration of operation is 1 ms, the available power supply current is approximately:

$$= CP\frac{dV_1}{dt} = 68 \ \mu F \times \frac{4.4 \ V}{1 \ ms} = 30 \ mA$$

BILATERAL CURRENT SOURCE

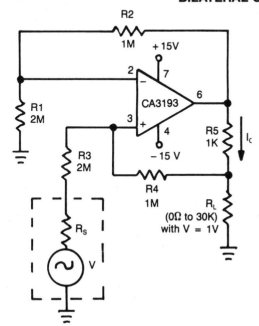

R2
1M + 15V

2 7

CA3193

6

3 + 4

R5
1K

I_c

− 15 V

R1
2M

R3
2M

R_s

V

R4
1M R_L
(0Ω to 30K)
with V = 1V

This circuit uses a CA3193 precision op amp to deliver a current independent of variations in R_L. With R1 set equal to R3, and R2 approximately equal to R4 + R5, the output current, I_L, is: V_{IN} (R4)/(R3) (R5). 500-μA load current is constant for load values from 0 to 3 Ω.

ALL RESISTORS ARE 1%
ALL RESISTANCE VALUES ARE IN OHMS
IF R1 = R3 AND R2 ≈ R4 + R5 THEN

I_L IS INDEPENDENT OF VARIATIONS IN R_L
FOR R_L VALUES OF 0Ω to 3KΩ WITH V = 1V

$$I_L = \frac{V \ R4}{R3 \ R5} = \frac{V \ 1M}{(2M)(1K)} = \frac{V}{2K} = 500\mu A$$

GE/RCA

Fig. 2-5

3- to 30-V UNIVERSAL POWER-SUPPLY MODULE

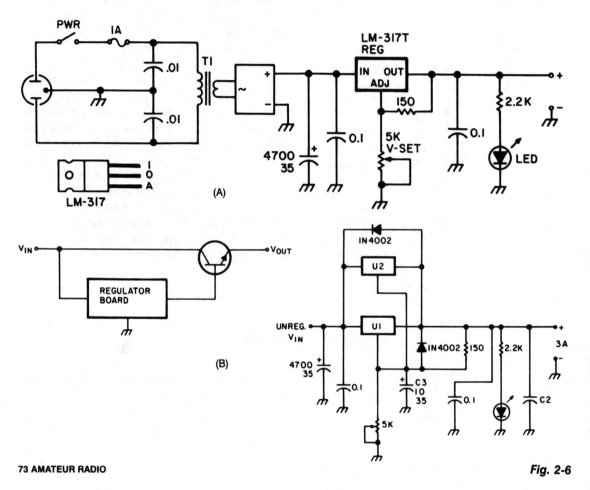

Fig. 2-6

U1, an LM317 adjustable regulator provides short-circuit protection and automatic current limiting at 1.5 A. The input voltage to the regulator is supplied by DB1, a 4-A 100 PIV full-wave bridge rectifier. Capacitor C1 provides initial filtering. U1 provides additional electronic filtering as part of the regulating function. The output level of the regulator is set by trim-pot R1. Bypass capacitors on the input and output of U1 prevent high-frequency oscillation. The current rating of the transformer must be at least 1.8 times the rated continuous-duty output of the supply. This means that a 1.5-A supply should use a 2.7-A transformer. For light or intermittent loads, a smaller 2.0-A transformer should suffice.

Wiring a second LM317, U2, in parallel with U1 is a quick and clean way to increase the current-limiting threshold to 3 A without sacrificing short-circuit protection. When more than 3 A is required, the regulator module can be used to drive the base of one or more pass-transistors (see Fig. 2-6B).

REGULATOR/CURRENT SOURCE

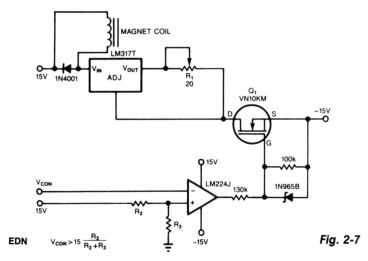

EDN $V_{CON} > 15 \dfrac{R_3}{R_2 + R_3}$

Fig. 2-7

The circuit powers the load via the regulator's input instead of its output. Because the regulator's output sees constant dummy load R1, it tries to consume a constant amount of current, no matter what the voltage across the actual load really is. Hence, the regulator's input serves as a constant-current source for the actual load. Power the circuit with any one of the commonly available ± 15- or ± 12-V supplies. The voltage dropped across the regulator and dummy load decreased the total compliance voltage of the circuit. You set the load's current with R1. The current equals $1.25 \ A/\Omega \times R_1$.

LOW-POWER SWITCHING REGULATOR

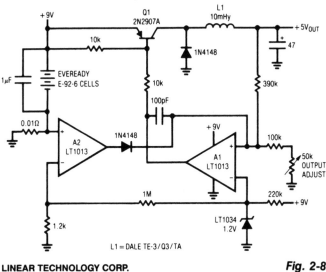

LINEAR TECHNOLOGY CORP.

Fig. 2-8

29

LOW-POWER SWITCHING REGULATOR (cont.)

A simple battery-powered switching regulator provides 5 V out from a 9-V source with 80% efficiency and 50-mA output capability. When Q1 is on, its collector voltage rises, forcing current through the inductor. The output voltage rises, causing A1's output to rise. Q1 cuts off and the output decays through the load. The 100-pF capacitor ensures clean switching. The cycle repeats when the output drops low enough for A1 to turn on Q1. The 1-μF capacitor ensures low battery impedance at high frequencies, preventing *sag* during switching.

VARIABLE VOLTAGE REGULATOR

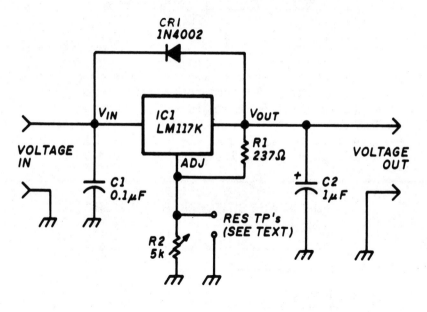

HAM RADIO   Fig. 2-9

The variable voltage regulator lets you adjust the output voltage of a fixed dc power supply between 1.2 and 37 Vdc, and will supply the output current in excess of 1.5 A. The circuit incorporates an LM117K three-terminal adjustable output positive voltage regulator in a TO-3 can. Thermal overload protection and short-circuit current-limiting constant with temperature are included in the package. Capacitor C1 reduces sensitivity to input line impedance, and C2 reduces excessive ringing. Diode CR1 prevents C2 from discharging through the IC during an output short.

SWITCHING POWER SUPPLY

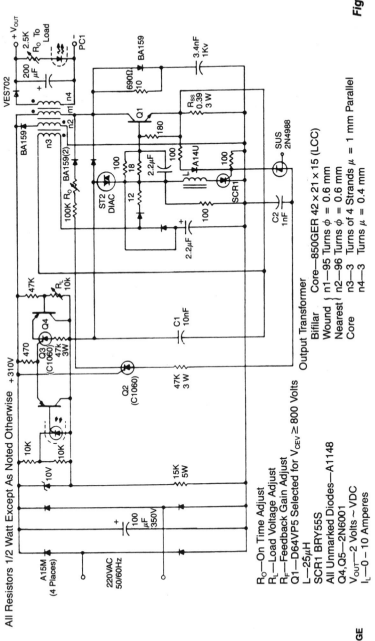

Fig. 2-10

This low-voltage high-current output, switching dc power supply is running off the 220-Vac input. In this circuit, an ST2 diac relaxation oscillator, Q3, C1, and the diac, initiates conduction of the output switching transistor Q1, the on-time of which is maintained constant by a separate timing/commutation network consisting of Q2, C2, SUS, and SCR 1. The output voltage, consequently, is dependent on the duty cycle. To compensate for unwanted variations of output voltage because of input voltage or load resistance fluctuations, an H11C wired as a linear-model unilateral pnp transistor in a stable differential amplifier configuration is connected into the galvanically isolated negative-feedback loop. The loop determines the duty cycle and hence the output voltage. Of further interest in this circuit is the use of several low-current, high-voltage, 400-V V_{DRM} thyristors (Q2, Q3), which are also used as pnp remote-base transistors. Short-circuit protection is assured by coupling Q1 collector-current feedback into the turn-off circuitry via R_{SS}.

31

100-kHz MULTIPLE-OUTPUT SWITCHING POWER SUPPLY

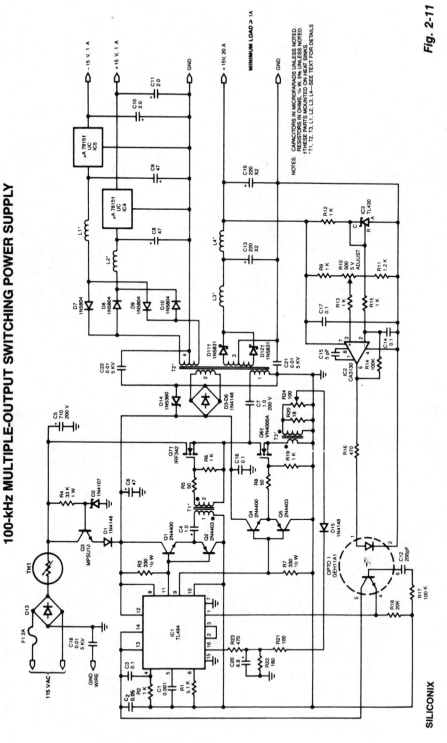

NOTES: CAPACITORS IN MICROFARADS UNLESS NOTED.
RESISTORS IN OHMS, ¼ W, 5% UNLESS NOTED.
†THESE PARTS MOUNTED ON HEAT SINKS.
*T1, T2, T3, L1, L2, L3, L4—SEE TEXT FOR DETAILS.

Fig. 2-11

SILICONIX

The power supply uses two VN4000A 400-V MOSPOWER FETs in a half-bridge power switch configuration. Outputs available are +5 V at 20 A and ±15 V (or ±12 V) at 1 A. Since linear three-terminal regulators are used for the low-current outputs, either ±12 V or ±15 V can be made available with a simple change in the transformer secondary windings. A TL494 switching regulator IC provides pulse-width modulation control and drive signals for the power supply. The upper MOSPOWER FET, Q7, in the power switch stage is driven by a simple transformer drive circuit. The lower MOS, Q6, since it is ground referenced, is directly driven from the control IC.

ISOLATED FEEDBACK POWER SUPPLY

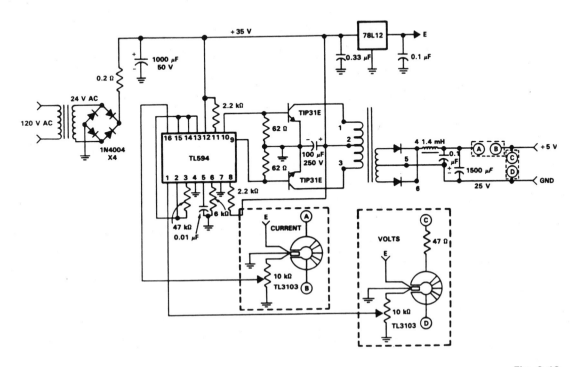

Fig. 2-12

Figure 2-12 is a power supply circuit using the isolated feedback capabilities of the TL3103 for both current and voltage sensing. This supply is powered from the ac power line and has an output of 5 V at 1.5 A. Both output voltage and current are sensed and the error voltages are applied to the error amplifiers of the TL594 PWM control IC. The 24-V transformer produces about 35 V at the $1000\text{-}\mu F$ filter capacitor. The 20-kHz switching frequency is set by the 6-kΩ resistor and the $0.01\text{-}\mu F$ capacitor on pins 6 and 5, respectively. The TL594 is set for push-pull operation by tying pin 13 high. The 5-V reference on pin 14 is tied to pin 15, which is the reference or the current error amplifier. The 5-V reference is also tied to pin 2 which is the reference for the output voltage error amplifier. The output voltage and current limit are set by adjustment of the 10-kΩ pots in the TL3103 error-sensing circuits. A pair of TIP31E npn transistors are used as switching transistors in a push-pull circuit.

DUAL-TRACKING REGULATOR

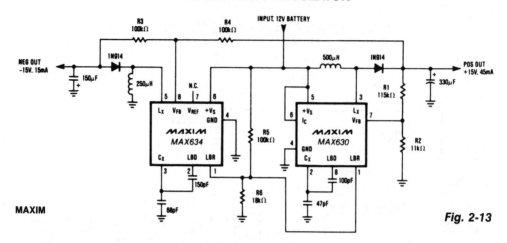

MAXIM

Fig. 2-13

A MAX634 inverting regulator is combined with a MAX630 to provide a dual tracking ± 15-V output from a 12-V battery. The reference for the − 15-V output is derived from the positive output via R3 and R4. Both regulators are set to maximize output power at low battery voltages by reducing the oscillator frequency, via LBR, when V_{BATT} falls to 8.5 V.

+ 15-V 1-A REGULATED POWER SUPPLY

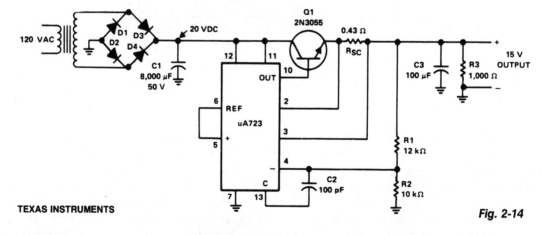

TEXAS INSTRUMENTS

Fig. 2-14

The supply receives + 20 Vdc from the rectifier/filter section. This is applied to pins 11 and 12 of the uA723, as well as to the collector of the 2N3055 series-pass transistor. The output voltage is sampled through R1 and R2, providing about 7 V with respect to ground at pin 4. The reference terminal at pin 6 is tied directly to pin 5, the noninverting input of the error amplifier. For fine trimming the output voltage, a potentiometer can be installed between R1 and R2. A 100-pF capacitor from pin 13 to pin 4 furnishes gain compensation for the amplifier.

Base drive to the 2N3055 pass transistor is furnished by pin 10 of the uA723. Since the desired output of the supply is 1 A, maximum current limit is set to 1.5 A by resistor R_{SC} whose value is 0.433 Ω.

A 100-μF electrolytic capacitor is used for ripple voltage reduction at the output. A 1-kΩ output resistor provides stability for the power supply under no-load conditions. The 2N3055 pass transistor must be mounted on an adequate heatsink.

– 15-V 1-A REGULATED POWER SUPPLY

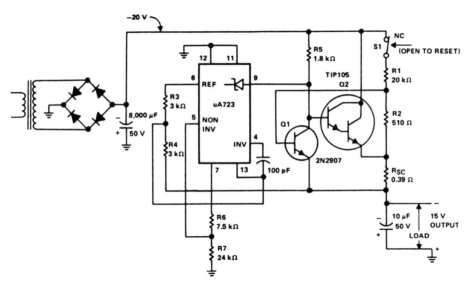

TEXAS INSTRUMENTS

Fig. 2-15

The supply receives – 20 V from the rectifier/filter which is fed to the collector of the Darlington pnp pass transistor, a TIP105. The base drive to the TIP105 is supplied through resistor R5. The base of the TIP105 is driven from V_z terminal at pin 9, which is the anode of a 6.2-V zener diode that connects to the emitter of the uA723 output control transistor. The method of providing the positive feedback required for foldback action is shown. This technique introduces positive feedback by increased current flow through resistors R1 and R2 under short-circuit conditions. This forward biases the base-emitter junction of the 2N2907 sensing transistor, which reduces base drive to the TIP105.

HAND-HELD TRANSCEIVER dc ADAPTER

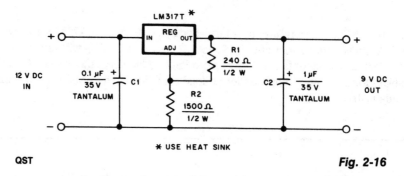

QST

Fig. 2-16

This dc adapter provides a regulated 9-V source for operating a Kenwood TR-2500 hand-held transceiver in the car. The LM317T's mounting tab is electrically connected to its output pin, so take this into account as you construct your version of the adapter. The LM317T regulator dissipates 2 or 3 W in this application, so mount it on a 1-×-2-inch piece of $1/8$-inch-thick aluminum heatsink.

LOW-DROPOUT 5-V REGULATOR

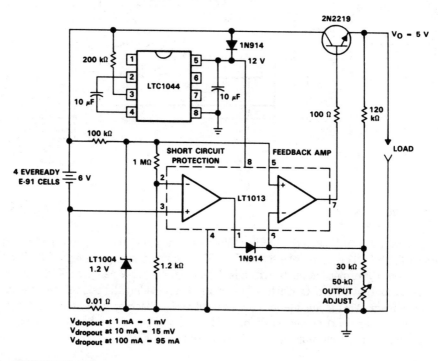

$V_{dropout}$ at 1 mA — 1 mV
$V_{dropout}$ at 10 mA — 15 mV
$V_{dropout}$ at 100 mA — 95 mA

TEXAS INSTRUMENTS

Fig. 2-17

TRIAC-CONTROLLED VOLTAGE DOUBLER

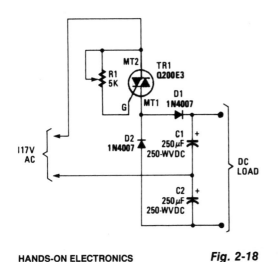

HANDS-ON ELECTRONICS   *Fig. 2-18*

HIGH-STABILITY 10-V REGULATOR

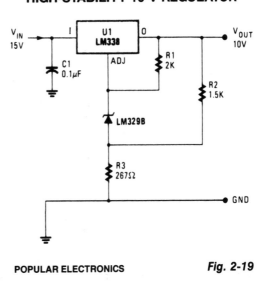

POPULAR ELECTRONICS   *Fig. 2-19*

VOLTAGE-CONTROLLED CURRENT SOURCE

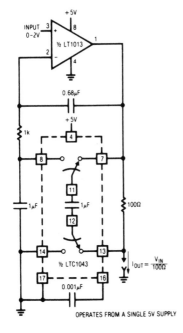

This is a simple, precise voltage-controlled current source. Bipolar supplies will permit bipolar output. Configurations featuring a grounded voltage-control source and a grounded load are usually more complex and depend upon several components for stability. In this circuit, accuracy and stability almost entirely depend upon the 100-Ω shunt.

LINEAR TECHNOLOGY CORP.   *Fig. 7-20*

LOW-POWER INVERTER

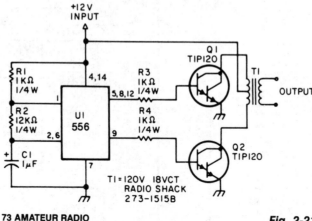

Fig. 2-21

This low-power inverter uses only 9 parts and turns 10 to 16 Vdc into 60-Hz, 115-V square-wave power to operate ac equipment up to 25 W. The first section of the 556 timer chip is wired as an astable oscillator with R2 and C1 setting the frequency. The output is available at pin 5. The second section is wired as a phase inverter. That output is available at pin 9. Resistors R3 and R4 keep output transistors Q1 and Q2 from loading down the oscillator. The two transistors drive the transformer push-pull fashion. When one transistor is biased-on, the other is cut-off. The transformer is a 120 V/18 VCT unit that is connected backwards, so that it steps the voltage up rather than down. Oscillator circuit U1, R1, R2, and C1 operates from about 4 to 16 V with a very stable output.

THREE-RAIL POWER SUPPLY

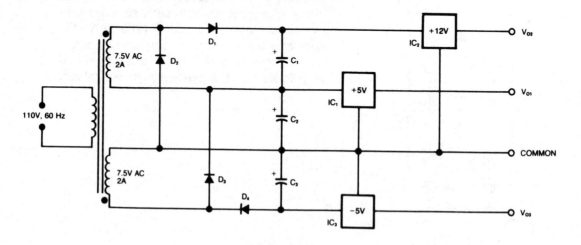

Fig. 2-22

This circuit generates three supply voltages using a minimum of components. Diodes D2 and D3 perform full-wave rectification, alternately charging capacitor C2 on both halves of the ac cycle. On the other hand, diode D1 with capacitor C1, and diode D4 with capacitor C3 each perform half-wave rectification. The full- and half-wave rectification arrangement is satisfactory for modest supply currents drawn from -5 and $+12$-V regulators IC3 and IC2. You can use this circuit as an auxiliary supply in an up-based instrument, for example, and avoid the less attractive alternatives of buying a custom-wound transformer, building a more complex supply, or using a secondary winding, say 18 Vac, and wasting power in the 5-V regulators.

PROGRAMMABLE POWER SUPPLY

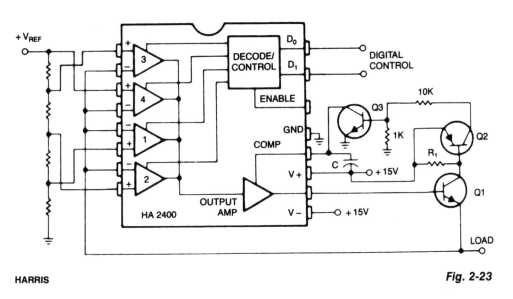

HARRIS

Fig. 2-23

Many systems require one or more relatively low-current voltage sources which can be programmed to a few predetermined levels. The circuit shown above produces positive output levels, but could be modified for negative or bipolar outputs. Q1 is the series regulator transistor, selected for the required current and power capability. R1, Q2, and Q3 form an optional short circuit protection circuit, with R1 chosen to drop about 0.7 V at the maximum output current. The compensation capacitor, C, should be chosen to keep the overshoot, when switching, to an acceptable level.

EFFICIENT NEGATIVE VOLTAGE REGULATOR

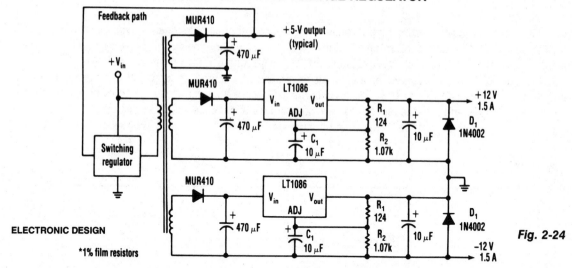

ELECTRONIC DESIGN

*1% film resistors

Fig. 2-24

One way to provide good negative-voltage regulation is with a low-dropout positive-voltage regulator operating from a well-isolated secondary winding of a switch-mode circuit transformer. The technique works with any positive-voltage regulator, although highest efficiency occurs with low-dropout types.

Under all loading conditions, the minimum voltage difference between the regulator V_{IN} and V_{OUT} pins must be at least 1.5 V, the LT1086's low-dropout voltage. If this requirement isn't met, the output falls out of regulation. Two programming resistors, R1 and R2, set the output voltage to 12 V, and the LT1086's servo the voltage between the output and its adjusting (ADJ) terminals to 1.25 V. Capacitor C1 improves ripple rejection, and protection diode D1 eliminates common-load problems.

Since a secondary winding is galvanically isolated, a regulator's 12 V output can be referenced to ground. Therefore, in the case of a negative-voltage output, the positive-voltage terminal of the regulator connects to ground, and the − 12 V output comes off the anode of D1. The V_{IN} terminal floats at 1.5 V or more above ground.

5 V-TO-ISOLATED 5 V (AT 20 mA) CONVERTER

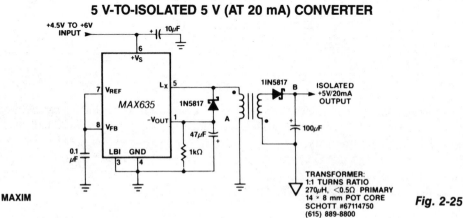

MAXIM

TRANSFORMER:
1:1 TURNS RATIO
270µH, <0.5Ω PRIMARY
14 × 8 mm POT CORE
SCHOTT #67114750
(615) 889-8800

Fig. 2-25

5 V-TO-ISOLATED 5 V (AT 20 mA) CONVERTER (cont.)

In this circuit, a negative output voltage dc-dc converter generates a −5-V output at pin A. In order to generate −5 V at point A, the primary of the transformer must fly back to a diode drop more negative than −5 V. If the transformer has a tightly coupled 1:1 turns ratio, there will be a 5 V plus a diode drop across the secondary. The 1N5817 rectifies this secondary voltage to generate an isolated 5-V output. The isolated output is not fully regulated since only the −5 V at point A is sensed by the MAX635.

POSITIVE REGULATOR WITH npn AND pnp BOOST

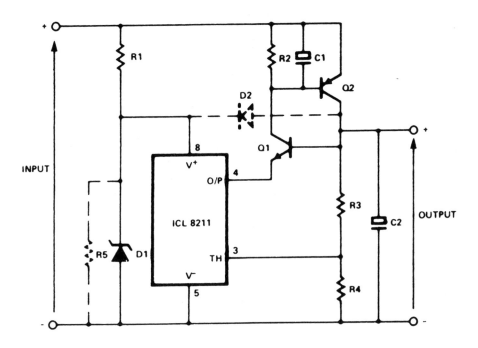

INTERSIL

Fig. 2-26

In the circuit, Q1 and Q2 are connected in the classic SCR or thyristor configuration. Where higher input voltages or minimum component count are required, the circuit for thyristor boost can be used. The thyristor is running in a linear mode with its cathode as the control terminal and its gate as the output terminal. This is known as the remote base configuration.

TRACKING PREREGULATOR

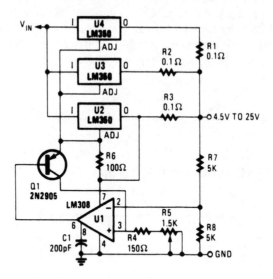

Fig. 2-27

ADJUSTABLE 10-A REGULATOR

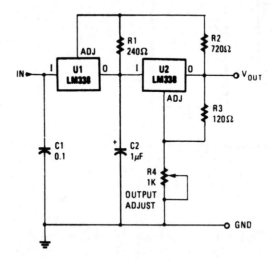

Fig. 2-28

LOW-COST LOW-DROPOUT LINEAR REGULATOR

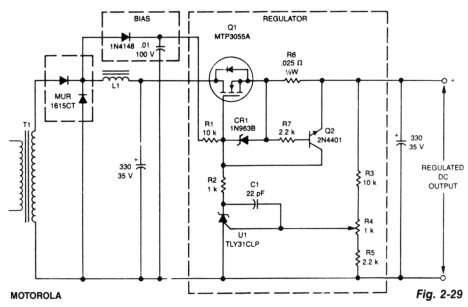

MOTOROLA

Fig. 2-29

This linear post regulator provides 12 V at 3 A. It employs TL431 reference U1 which, without additional amplification, drives TMOS MTP3055A gate Q1 series pass regulator. Bias voltage is applied through R1 to Q1's gate, which is protected against overvoltage by diode CR1. Frequency compensation for closed-loop stability is provided by C1.

Key performance features are:

Dropout voltage:	0.6 V	Load regulation:	10 mV
Line regulation:	± 5 mV	Output ripple:	10 mV pk-pk

VOLTAGE DOUBLER

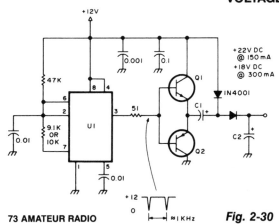

This circuit drives relays of 24 and 18 Vdc from a 12-V power supply. Use this circuit with almost any pnp or npn power transistor.

Parts: U1: NE 555 timer. C1 and C2: 50 μF/ 25 Vdc. Q1: TIP29, TIP120, 2N4922, TIP61, TIP110, or 2N4921. Q2: TIP30, TIP125, 2N4919, TIP62, TIP115, or 2N4918.

73 AMATEUR RADIO

Fig. 2-30

SAFE CONSTANT-CURRENT SOURCE

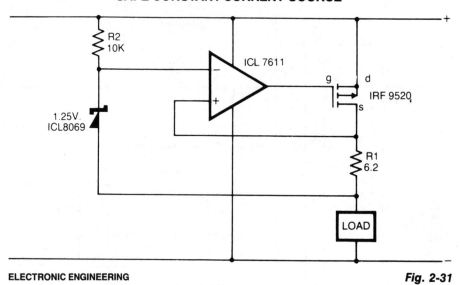

ELECTRONIC ENGINEERING

Fig. 2-31

In the circuit shown, a CMOS op amp controls the current through a p-channel HEXFET power transistor to maintain a constant voltage across R1. The current is given by: $I = V_{REF}/R_1$. The advantages of this configuration are: (a) in the event of a component failure, the load current is limited by R1; and (b) the overhead voltage needed by the op amp and the HEXFET is extremely low.

LOW-COST 3-A SWITCHING REGULATOR

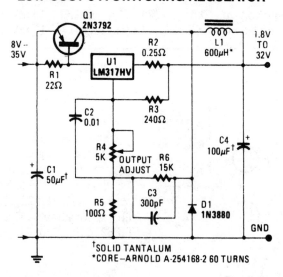

POPULAR ELECTRONICS

Fig. 2-32

50-W OFF-LINE SWITCHING POWER SUPPLY

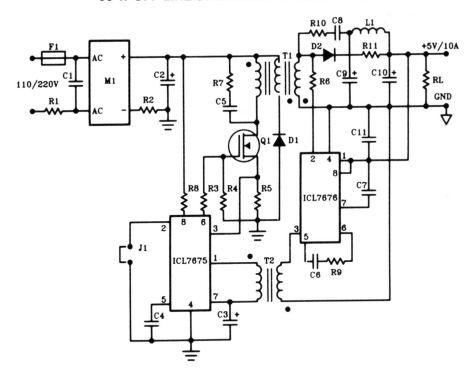

Component Values Table

C1	0.022 µF/400V	R1	100Ω at 25°C	L1	25 µH
C2	470 µF/250V	R2	1Ω/1W	D1	1N4937
C3	470 µF/16V	R3	10Ω/0.25W	D2	MBR1035
C4	220 pF/100V	R4	100 kΩ/0.25W	T1	Lp = 9 mH, n = 1:15
C5	470 pF/500V	R5	0.33Ω/1W	T2	50 µH, n = 1:3
C6	2200 pF/500V	R6	10 kΩ/0.25W	F1	Fuse 1 A/SB
C7	270 pF/500V	R7	390Ω/2W	M1	Diode Bridge
C8	39 pF/500V	R8	22 kΩ/10W	Q1	BUZ80A/IXTP4N80
C9	11,000 µF/6.3V	R9	68Ω/0.25W		(220VAC)
C10	10 µF/16V	R10	10Ω/0.5W	Q1	GE IRF823
C11	0.047 µF/10V	R11	3.3Ω/0.5W		(110VAC)
		RL	5Ω/10W		

INTERSIL

Fig. 2-33

The schematic shows a 50-W power supply with a 5-V 10-A output. It is a flyback converter operating in the continuous mode. The circuit features a primary side and secondary side controller with full-protection from fault conditions such as overcurrent. After the fault condition has been removed, the power supply will enter the soft-start cycle before recommencing normal operation.

POSITIVE REGULATOR WITH pnp BOOST

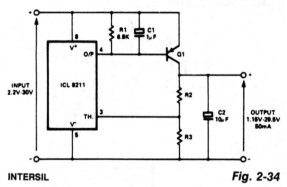

Fig. 2-34

The IC8211 provides the voltage reference and regulator amplifier, while Q1 is the series pass transistor. R1 defines the output current of the IC8211, while C1 and C2 provide loop stability and also act to suppress feedthrough of input transients to the output supply. R2 and R3 determine the output voltage as follows:

$$V_{OUT} = 1.5 \times \frac{R_2 + R_3}{R_3}$$

In addition, the values of R2 and R3 are chosen to provide a small amount of standing current in Q1, which gives additional stability margin to the circuit. Where accurate setting of the output voltage is required, either R2 or R3 can be made adjustable. If R2 is made adjustable, the output voltage will vary linearly with the shaft angle; however, if the potentiometer wiper was to open the circuit, the output voltage would rise. In general, therefore, it is better to make R3 adjustable, since this gives fail-safe operation.

LOW FORWARD-DROP RECTIFIER CIRCUIT

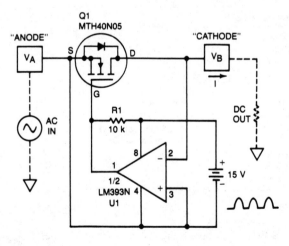

Fig. 2-35

A TMOS power FET, Q1, and an LM393 comparator provide a high-efficiency rectifier circuit. When V_A exceeds V_B, U1's output becomes high and Q1 conducts. Conversely, when V_B exceeds V_A, the comparator output becomes low and Q1 does not conduct.

The forward drop is determined by Q1's on resistance and current I. The MTH40N05 has an ON resistance of 0.028 Ω; for $I = 10$ A, the forward drop is less than 0.3 V. Typically, the best Schottky diodes do not even begin conducting below a few hundred mV.

LOW-RIPPLE POWER SUPPLY

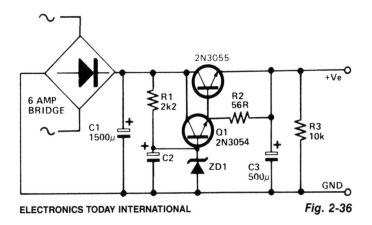

2N3055

6 AMP BRIDGE

C1 1500μ

R1 2k2

R2 56R

Q1 2N3054

C2

ZD1

C3 500μ

R3 10k

+Ve

GND

ELECTRONICS TODAY INTERNATIONAL

Fig. 2-36

This circuit can be used where a high current is required with a low-ripple voltage (such as in a high-powered class AB amplifier when high-quality reproduction is necessary). Q1, Q2, and R2 can be regarded as a power-Darlington transistor. ZD1 and R1 provide a reference voltage at the base of Q1. ZD1 should be chosen thus: $ZD_1 = V_{out} - 1.2$. C2 can be chosen for the degree of smoothness as its value is effectively multiplied by the combined gains of Q1/Q2, if 100 μF is chosen for C2, assuming minimum hfe for Q1 and Q2, $C = 100 \times 15(Q1) \times 25(Q2) = 37,000$ μF.

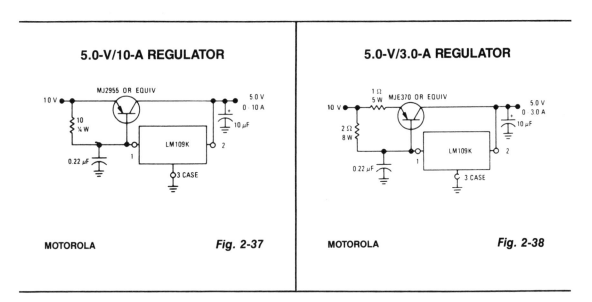

5.0-V/10-A REGULATOR

MJ2955 OR EQUIV

10 V

10 ¼ W

0.22 μF

LM109K

1

3 CASE

2

5.0 V 0 - 10 A

10 μF

MOTOROLA

Fig. 2-37

5.0-V/3.0-A REGULATOR

1 Ω 5 W   MJE370 OR EQUIV

10 V

2 Ω 8 W

0.22 μF

LM109K

1

3 CASE

2

5.0 V 0 - 3.0 A

10 μF

MOTOROLA

Fig. 2-38

BENCH-TOP POWER SUPPLY

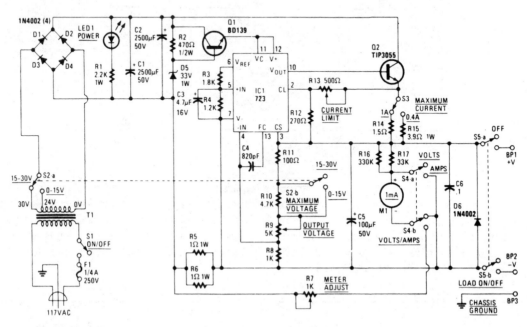

RADIO-ELECTRONICS

Fig. 2-39

A tapped transformer drives a diode bridge (D1 – D4) and two 2500-μF filter capacitors (C1 and C2), that provide a no-load voltage of 37 or 47 V, depending upon the position of switch S2a. The unregulated dc is then fed to a preregulator stage, which is composed of Q1 and D5. Those components protect IC1 (the 723) from an over-voltage condition; the 723 can't handle more than 40 V. The LED (LED1) and its 2.2-kΩ current-limiting resistor (R1) provide on/off indication. The current through the LED varies slightly according to the transformer tap selected, but that's of no real consequence. The series-pass transistor in IC1 drives voltage-follower Q2, providing current amplification. The transistor can handle lots of power. It has a maximum collector current of 15 A and a maximum V_{CE} of 70 V, both of which are more than adequate for our supply.

VARIABLE CURRENT SOURCE (100 mA TO 2 A)

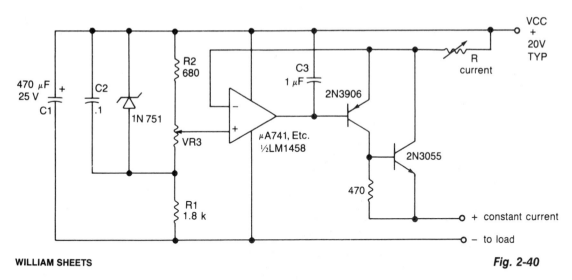

WILLIAM SHEETS

Fig. 2-40

The output current is set by the resistor R in the collector of Tr2, which can be varied to offer a range of output currents from 100 mA to 2 A with fine control by means of VR3, which varies the reference voltage to the noninverting input of the op amp. The feedback path from the output to the inverting input of the op amp maintains a constant voltage across R, which is equal to $(V_{CC} - V_{IN})$ and hence a constant current to the load given by $(V_{CC} - V_{IN})/R$.

BASIC SINGLE-SUPPLY VOLTAGE REGULATOR

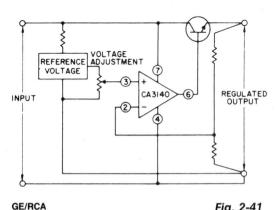

The circuit uses a CA3140 BiMOS op amp that is capable of supplying a regulated output that can be adjusted from essentially 0 to 24 V.

GE/RCA

Fig. 2-41

8-A REGULATED POWER SUPPLY FOR OPERATING MOBILE EQUIPMENT

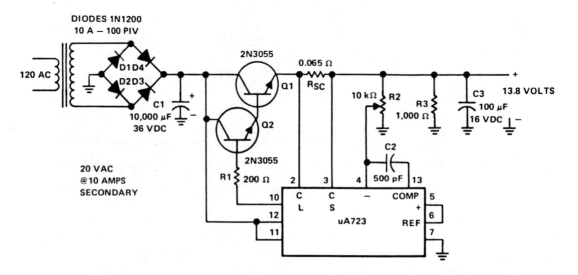

TEXAS INSTRUMENTS

Fig. 2-42

This supply is powered by a transformer that operates from 120 Vac on the primary and provides approximately 20 Vac on the secondary. Four 10-A diodes with a 100-PIV rating are used in a full-wave bridge rectifier. A 10,000-μF/36-Vdc capacitor completes the filtering and provides 28 Vdc. The dc voltage is fed to the collectors of the Darlington connecting the 2N3055's. Base drive for the pass transistors is from pin 10 of the μA723 through a 200-Ω current-limiting resistor, R1. The reference terminal (pin 6) is tied directly to the non-inverting input of the error amplifier (pin 5), providing 7.15 V for comparison.

The inverting input to the error amplifier (pin 4) is fed from the center arm of a 10-kΩ potentiometer connected across the output of the supply. This control is set for the desired output voltage of 13.8 V. Compensation of the error amplifier is accomplished with a 500-pF capacitor connected from pin 13 to pin 4. If the power supply should exceed 8 A or develop a short circuit, the μA723 regulator will bias the transistors to cut off and the output voltage will drop to near zero until the short-circuit condition is corrected.

LOW-VOLTAGE REGULATORS WITH SHORT-CIRCUIT PROTECTION

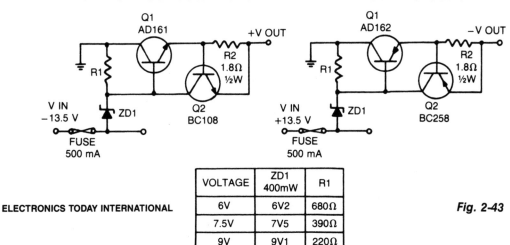

VOLTAGE	ZD1 400mW	R1
6V	6V2	680Ω
7.5V	7V5	390Ω
9V	9V1	220Ω

ELECTRONICS TODAY INTERNATIONAL

Fig. 2-43

These short-circuit protected regulators give 6, 7.5, and 9 V from an automobile battery supply of 13.5 V nominal; however, they will function just as well if connected to a smoothed dc output from a transformer/rectifier circuit. Two types are shown for both positive and negative ground systems. The power transistors can be mounted on the heatsink without a mica insulating spacer, thus allowing for greater cooling efficiency. Both circuits are protected against overload or short-circuits. The current cannot exceed 330 mA. Under normal operating conditions the voltage across R2 does not rise above the 500 mV necessary to turn Q2 on and the circuit behaves as if only Q1 was present. If excessive current is drawn, Q2 turns on and cuts off Q1, protecting the regulating transistor. The table gives the values of R1 for different zener voltages.

HIGH-STABILITY 1-A REGULATOR

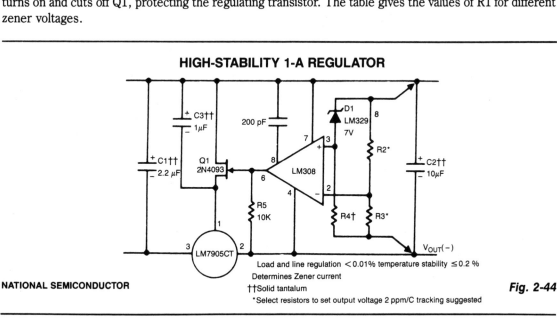

Load and line regulation <0.01% temperature stability ≤0.2 %

Determines Zener current

††Solid tantalum

*Select resistors to set output voltage 2 ppm/C tracking suggested

NATIONAL SEMICONDUCTOR

Fig. 2-44

HIGH-CURRENT INDUCTORLESS SWITCHING REGULATOR

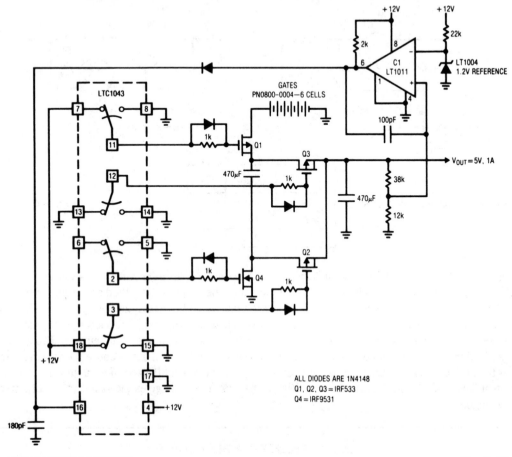

Fig. 2-45

The LTC10432 switched-capacitor building block provides nonoverlapping complementary drive to the Q1 to Q4 power MOSFETs. The MOSFETs are arranged so that C1 and C2 are alternately placed in series and then parallel. During the series phase, the +12-V battery's current flows through both capacitors, charging them, and furnishing load current. During the parallel phase, both capacitors deliver current to the load. Q1 and Q2 receive similar drive from pins 3 and 11. The diode-resistor networks provide additional nonoverlapping drive characteristics, preventing simultaneous drive to the series-parallel phase switches. Normally, the output would be one-half of the supply voltage, but C1 and its associated components close a feedback loop, forcing the output to 5 V. With the circuit in the series phase, the output heads rapidly positive. When the output exceeds 5 V, C1 trips, forcing the LTC1043 oscillator pin, trace D, high; this truncates the LTC1043's triangular-wave oscillator cycle. The circuit is forced into the parallel phase and the output coasts down slowly, until the next LTC1043 clock cycle begins. C1's output diode prevents the triangle down-slope from being affected and the 100-pF capacitor provides sharp transitions. The loop regulates the output to 5 V by feedback controlling the turn-off point of the series phase.

200-kHz SWITCHING REGULATOR

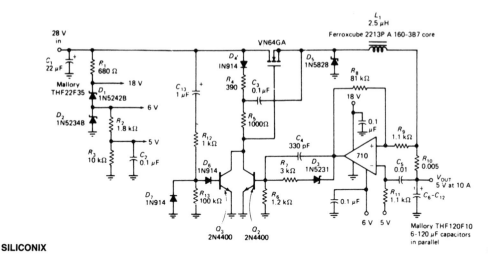

SILICONIX

Fig. 2-46

This circuit provides a regulated dc with less than 100 mV of ripple for microprocessor applications. Necessary operating voltages are taken from the bleeder resistor network connected across the unregulated 28-V supply. The output of the LM710 comparator (actually an oscillator running at 200 kHz) is fed through a level-shifting circuit to the base of bipolar transistor Q2. This transistor is part of a bootstrap circuit necessary to turn the power MOSFET full on in totem-pole MOSFET arrays.

5-V 0.5-A POWER SUPPLY

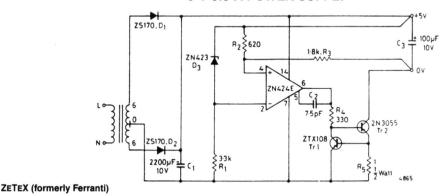

ZETEX (formerly Ferranti)

Fig. 2-47

The circuit is essentially a constant source modified by the feedback components R2 and R3 to give a constant voltage output. The output of the ZN424E need only be 2 V above the negative rail, by placing the load in the collector of the output transistor Tr2. The current circuit is achieved by Tr1 and R5. This simple circuit has the following performance characteristics: Output noise and ripple (full load) = 1 mV rms. Load regulation (0 to 0.5 A) = 0.1%. Temperature coefficient = ± 100 ppm/°C. Current limit = 0.65 A.

3-W SWITCHING-REGULATOR CIRCUIT

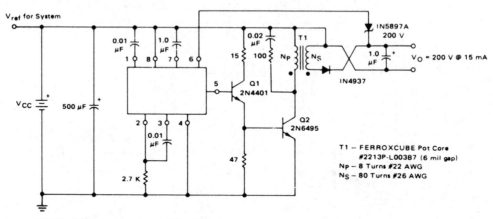

3-Watt Switching Regulator - converts 5 V to 200 V for gas discharge displays such as Burroughs Panaplex and Beckman.

MOTOROLA

Fig. 2-48

REGULATED SPLIT POWER SUPPLIES FROM A SINGLE SUPPLY

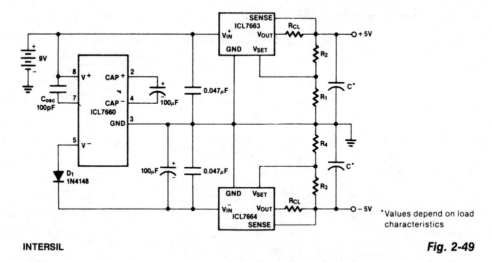

*Values depend on load characteristics

INTERSIL

Fig. 2-49

The oscillation frequency of the ICL7660 is reduced by the external oscillator capacitor so that it inverts the battery voltage more efficiently.

SWITCHING STEP-DOWN REGULATOR

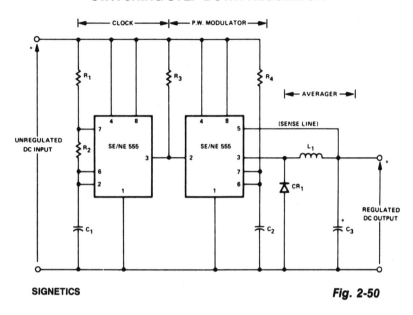

SIGNETICS

Fig. 2-50

SINGLE-ENDED REGULATOR

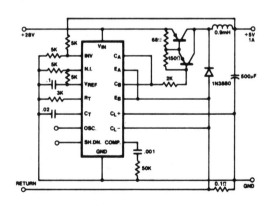

In this conventional single-ended regulator circuit, the two outputs of the SG1524 are connected in parallel for effective 0 – 90% duty-cycle modulation. The use of an output inductor requires an RC phase-compensation network for loop stability.

SIGNETICS

Fig. 2-51

± 50-V PUSH-PULL SWITCHED-MODE CONVERTER

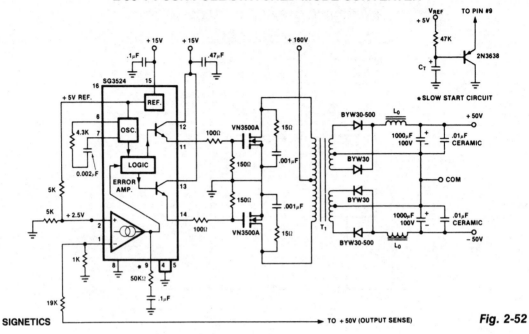

Fig. 2-52

SIGNETICS

TO + 50V (OUTPUT SENSE)

5-V/0.5-A BUCK CONVERTER

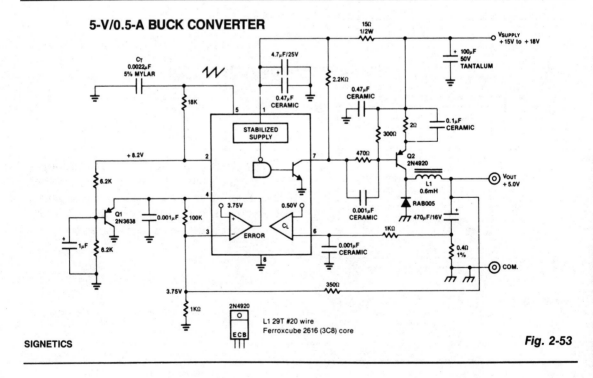

L1 29T #20 wire
Ferroxcube 2616 (3C8) core

Fig. 2-53

SIGNETICS

SLOW TURN-ON 15-V REGULATOR

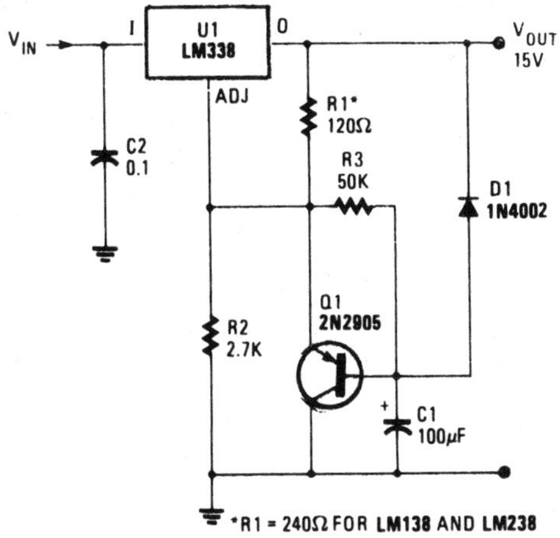

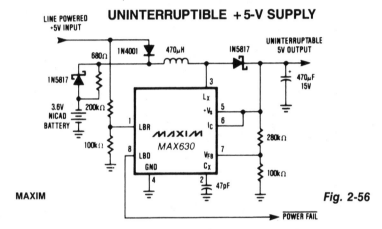

POPULAR ELECTRONICS *Fig. 2-54*

ac VOLTAGE REGULATOR

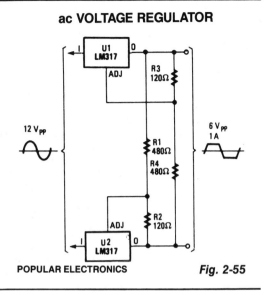

POPULAR ELECTRONICS *Fig. 2-55*

UNINTERRUPTIBLE +5-V SUPPLY

MAXIM *Fig. 2-56*

This circuit provides a continuous supply of regulated +5 V, with automatic switch-over between line power and battery backup. When the line-powered input voltage is at +5 V, it provides 4.4 V to the MAX630 and trickle charges the battery. If the line-powered input falls below the battery voltage, the 3.6-V battery supplies power to the MAX630, which boosts the battery voltage up to +5 V, thus maintaining a continuous supply to the uninterruptible +5-V bus. Since the +5-V output is always supplied through the MAX630, there are no power spikes or glitches during power transfer. The MAX630's low-battery detector monitors the line-powered +5 V, and the LBD output can be used to shut down unnecessary sections of the system during power failures. Alternatively, the low-battery detector could monitor the NiCad battery voltage and provide warning of power loss when the battery is nearly discharged. Unlike battery backup systems that use 9-V batteries, this circuit does not need +12 or +15 V to recharge the battery. Consequently, it can be used to provide +5-V backup on modules or circuit cards which only have 5 V available.

STAND-BY POWER FOR NONVOLATILE CMOS RAMs

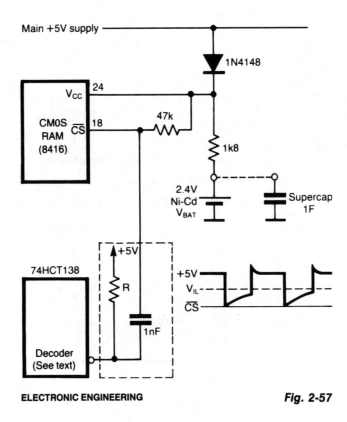

ELECTRONIC ENGINEERING

Fig. 2-57

To prevent loss of data when a CMOS RAM is switched from normal operation ($V_{CC} = 5$ V) to stand-by mode ($V_{CC} = V_{BAT}$), the CS pin must go near the V_{CC} rail at all times. Ac coupling to the chip select is made through capacitor C, breaking the dc current path between V_{CC} (and hence V_{BAT}) and the decoder output. So, whatever the impedance state of the decoder in power down, the battery will provide current only for the RAM, which is low enough to keep the voltage at CS near to V_{CC}.

5-V SUPPLY WITH STABILIZED MOMENTARY BACKUP

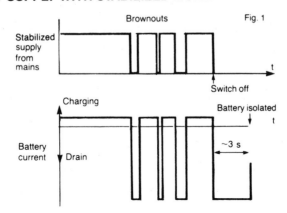

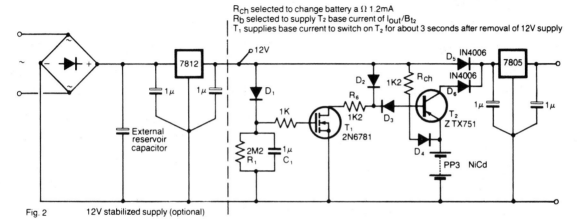

R_{ch} selected to change battery a Ω 1.2mA
R_b selected to supply T_2 base current of I_{out}/B_{t2}
T_1 supplies base current to switch on T_2 for about 3 seconds after removal of 12V supply

Fig. 2   12V stabilized supply (optional)

Fig. 2-58

This circuit protects microprocessor systems from "brownouts" without the expense of an uninterruptible power supply. Designed around a small 9-V nickel-cadmium battery, the circuit continues to provide a constant 5-V output during brownouts of up to a few seconds. Load currents of up to 500 mA can be drawn using the components shown. With this mains-derived supply present, D5 is forward-biased so that the stabilized supply powers the 5-V regulator and hence the circuitry to be protected. FET T1 is held on by D1, its drain current being provided from the dc supply via R_b and D2. Diode D3 is reverse-biased so that T2 is off, and the battery is isolated from D6. R_{CH} and D4 serve to trickle charge the battery with approximately 1.2 mA.

When the 12-V supply is removed, R1 and C1 initially keep T1 switched on. D3 is now forward-biased so that T1 drain current is drawn via R_b, D3, and T2 from the battery. This switches T2 on, allowing the load circuitry to draw current from the battery via D6 and the 5-V regulator. After a few seconds, C1 has discharged (via R1) so that V_{gs} falls below the threshold value for the FET, and T1 switches off. There is then no path for T2 base current so that it also switches off, isolating the battery.

UNINTERRUPTIBLE POWER SUPPLY FOR PERSONAL COMPUTERS

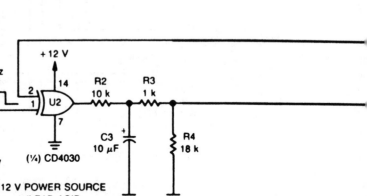

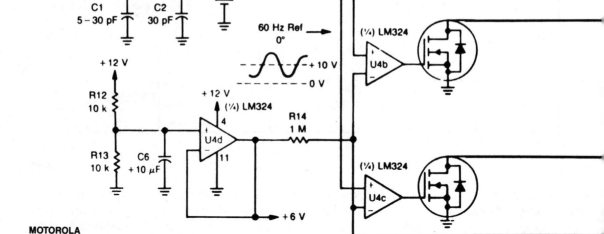

MOTOROLA

The UPS is basically an ac inverter that is powered by a 12-V, lead-acid automobile battery. During power outages, it can supply several minutes of power for an average personal computer. It incorporates a crystal-controlled 60-Hz time base so that a computer with a real-time clock can maintain its accuracy. It isolates the ac line from the computer, so it can be used to operate sensitive electronic equipment on noisy power sources.

Two MTM60N06 Power FETs (Q1 and Q2) alternately switch current through a center-tapped 120-V to 12-V filament transformer (T1) with its primary and secondary reversed. The 120-V output is compared with a 60-Hz reference in a closed-loop configuration that maintains a constant output at optimum efficiency.

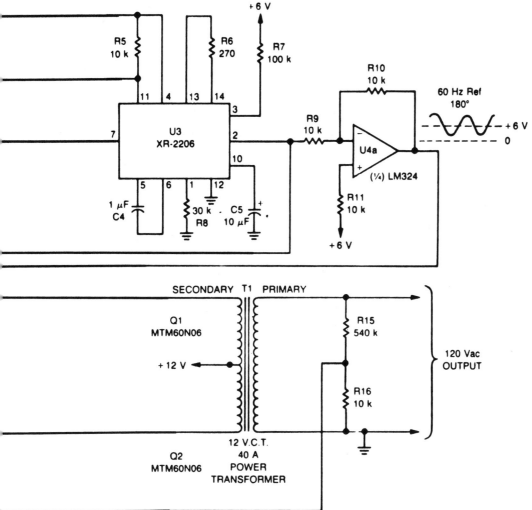

Fig. 2-59

A 60-Hz reference frequency is derived from a crystal oscillator and divider circuit, U1. An inexpensive 3.58-MHz color-burst crystal provides the time base that can be accurately adjusted by C1. The 60-Hz output from U1 is applied to the exclusive-OR gate, U2, and then to the XR-2206 function generator (U3) that converts the square wave into a sine wave. U2 and U3 form a phase-locked loop that synchronizes the sine-wave output of U3 with the 60-Hz square-wave reference of U1. The sine wave is then inverted by op amp U4a so that two signals 180° out of phase can be applied to U4b and U4c, which drive Q1 and Q2. As a result of the closed-loop configuration of the drive circuits, Q1 and Q2 conduct only during the upper half of the sine wave. Therefore, one TMOS device conducts during the first half of the sine wave and the other conducts during the second half.

90-Vrms VOLTAGE REGULATOR USING A PUT

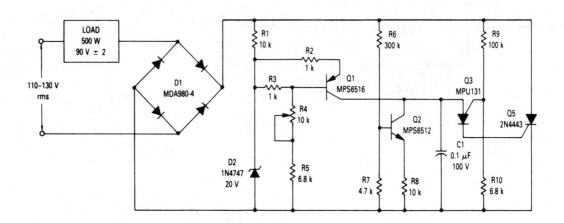

MOTOROLA

Fig. 2-60

The circuit is an open-loop rms voltage regulator that will provide 500 watts of power at 90 Vrms with good regulation for an input voltage range of 110 to 130 Vrms. With the input voltage applied, capacitor C1 charges until the firing point of Q3 is reached causing it to fire. This turns Q5 on which allows current to flow through the load. As the input voltage increases, the voltage across R10 increases, which increases the firing point of Q3. This delays the firing of Q3 because C1 now has to charge to a higher voltage before the peak-point voltage is reached. Thus, the output voltage is held fairly constant by delaying the firing of Q5 as the input voltage increases. For a decrease in the input voltage, the reverse occurs.

SWITCH-MODE POWER SUPPLY

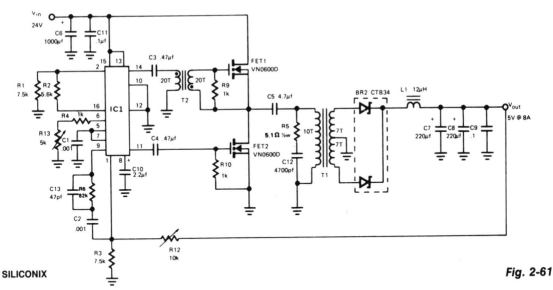

SILICONIX

Fig. 2-61

This buck-derived circuit provides up to 8 A at 5 Vdc operating off 24 to 32 Vdc. The two power MOS-FETs in the circuit conduct alternately for equal periods. Switching frequency is 150 kHz, set by the PWM125 controller. The output of the two MOSFETs is transformed to a low-voltage level, then rectified. Efficiency of the circuit is 75% when operated in a 22- to 32-V range. Efficiency approaches 90% with higher voltage inputs.

MICROPOWER BANDGAP REFERENCE SUPPLY

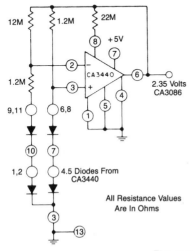

GE/RCA

Fig. 2-62

The circuit uses a CA3440 BiMOS op amp and a CA3086 transistor array. The no-load current from 5-V supply is 1.5 μA. Load current can go as high as 200 μA and still maintain output voltage regulation within 0.05%.

± 50-V FEED FORWARD SWITCH-MODE CONVERTER

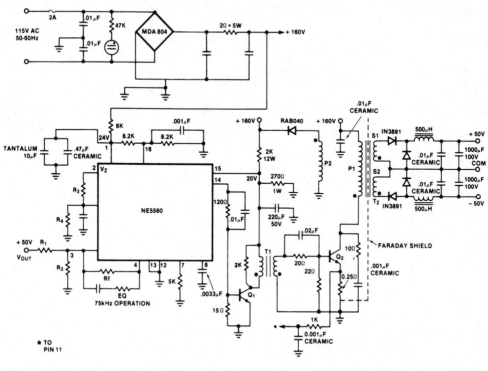

SIGNETICS

Fig. 2-63

TRAVELLER'S SHAVER ADAPTER

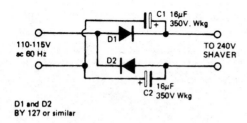

D1 and D2
BY 127 or similar

ELECTRONICS TODAY INTERNATIONAL   *Fig. 2-64*

Many countries have 115-V mains supplies. This can be a problem if your electric shaver is designed for 220/240 V only. This simple rectifier voltage doubler enables motor-driven 240-V shavers to be operated at full speed from a 115-V supply. As the output voltage is dc, the circuit can only be used to drive small ac/dc motors. It cannot be used, for example, to operate vibrator-type shavers or radios, unless the latter are ac/dc operated.

100-V/0.25-A SWITCH-MODE CONVERTER

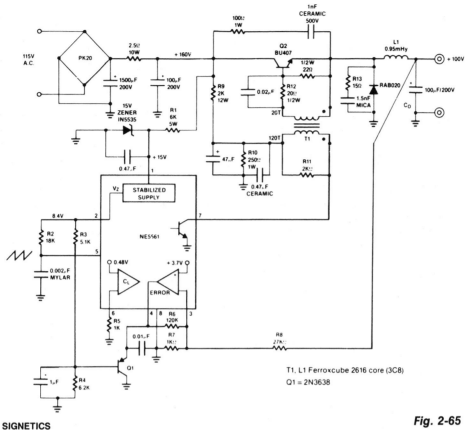

T1, L1 Ferroxcube 2616 core (3C8)
Q1 = 2N3638

SIGNETICS

Fig. 2-65

VOLTAGE REGULATOR

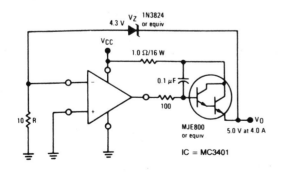

$V_O = V_Z + 0.6$ Vdc

NOTE 1: R is used to bias the zener.

NOTE 2: If the Zener TC is positive, and equal in magnitude to the negative TC of the input to the operational amplifier (≈ 2.0 mV/°C), the output is zero-TC. A 7.0-Volt Zener will give approximately zero-TC.

MOTOROLA

Fig. 2-66

DUAL-POLARITY POWER SUPPLY

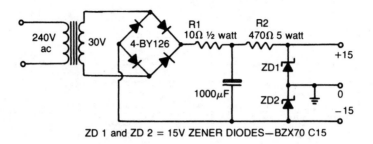

ZD 1 and ZD 2 = 15V ZENER DIODES—BZX70 C15

ELECTRONICS TODAY INTERNATIONAL

Fig. 2-67

This simple circuit gives a positive and negative supply from a single transformer winding and one full-wave bridge. Two zener diodes in series provide the voltage division and their centerpoint is grounded. (The filter capacitor must not be grounded via its case.)

5.0-V/6.0-A/25-kHz SWITCHING REGULATOR WITH SEPARATE ULTRASTABLE REFERENCE

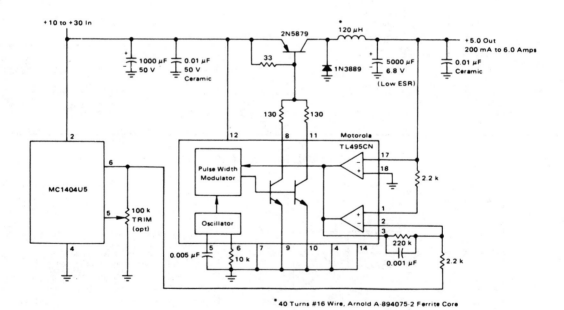

*40 Turns #16 Wire, Arnold A-894075-2 Ferrite Core

MOTOROLA

Fig. 2-68

MOBILE VOLTAGE REGULATOR

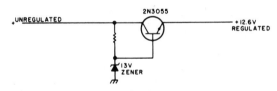

73 AMATEUR RADIO

Fig. 2-69

This simple mobile voltage regulator circuit might save your two meter or CB transceiver if the voltage regulator fails. The 2N3055 should be heat-sinked if current drawn by the rig is in excess of 2 A on transmit. This circuit will do little under normal operating conditions, but it could save expensive equipment if the vehicle's electrical system loses regulation.

NEGATIVE SWITCHING REGULATOR

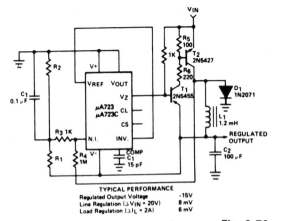

TYPICAL PERFORMANCE
Regulated Output Voltage	-15V
Line Regulation ($\Delta V_{IN} = 20V$)	8 mV
Load Regulation ($\Delta I_L = 2A$)	6 mV

INTERSIL

Fig. 2-70

POSITIVE FLOATING REGULATOR

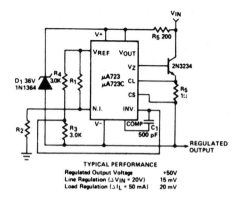

TYPICAL PERFORMANCE
Regulated Output Voltage	+50V
Line Regulation ($\Delta V_{IN} = 20V$)	15 mV
Load Regulation ($\Delta I_L = 50$ mA)	20 mV

INTERSIL

Fig. 2-72

POSITIVE SWITCHING REGULATOR

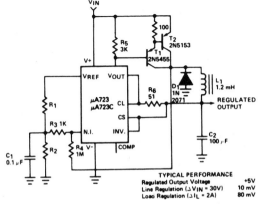

TYPICAL PERFORMANCE
Regulated Output Voltage	+5V
Line Regulation ($\Delta V_{IN} = 30V$)	10 mV
Load Regulation ($\Delta I_L = 2A$)	80 mV

INTERSIL

Fig. 2-71

NEGATIVE FLOATING REGULATOR

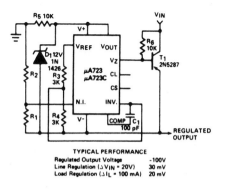

TYPICAL PERFORMANCE
Regulated Output Voltage	-100V
Line Regulation ($\Delta V_{IN} = 20V$)	30 mV
Load Regulation ($\Delta I_L = 100$ mA)	20 mV

INTERSIL

Fig. 2-73

NEGATIVE VOLTAGE REGULATOR

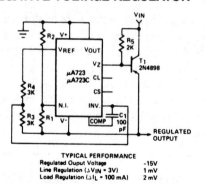

TYPICAL PERFORMANCE

Regulated Ouput Voltage	-15V
Line Regulation (ΔV_{IN} = 3V)	1 mV
Load Regulation (ΔI_L = 100 mA)	2 mV

INTERSIL   *Fig. 2-74*

– 15-V NEGATIVE REGULATOR

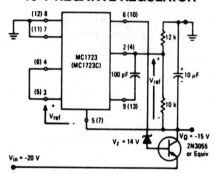

MOTOROLA   *Fig. 2-75*

SLOW TURN-ON 15-V REGULATOR

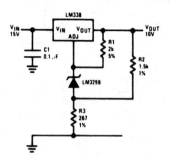

NATIONAL SEMICONDUCTOR   *Fig. 2-76*

HIGH-STABILITY 10-V REGULATOR

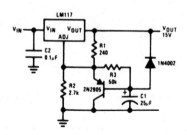

NATIONAL SEMICONDUCTOR   *Fig. 2-77*

5-V/1-A SWITCHING REGULATOR

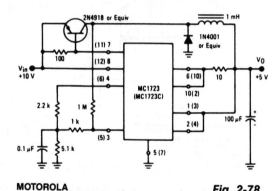

MOTOROLA   *Fig. 2-78*

15-V/1-A REGULATOR
WITH REMOTE SENSE

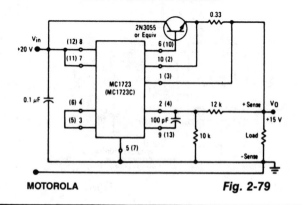

MOTOROLA   *Fig. 2-79*

INCREASING THE POWER RATING OF ZENER DIODES

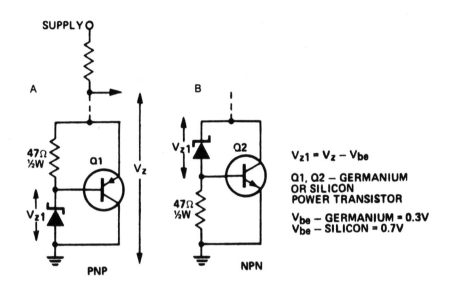

$V_{z1} = V_z - V_{be}$

Q1, Q2 – GERMANIUM
OR SILICON
POWER TRANSISTOR

V_{be} – GERMANIUM = 0.3V
V_{be} – SILICON = 0.7V

ELECTRONICS TODAY INTERNATIONAL

Fig. 2-80

A power transistor can be used to provide a high-powered zener voltage from a low-wattage zener. A 400-mW zener can be used where a 10-W zener is required or a 1-W zener can be used where a 50- to 80-W zener is required by using appropriate transistors for Q1 and Q2 (in the circuits shown). Where low rating is required, Q1 would be an ASZ 15 (germanium) or an AY9140 (silicon). Q2 could be a 2N2955 (silicon). For higher powers, Q1 should be an ASZ18 (germanium) or a 2N2955 (silicon), and Q2 a 2N3055 (silicon) or an AY8149 (silicon). A heatsink on the transistor is required. The circuit in A has the advantage that power transistors can be bolted directly on to a chassis, which can serve as a heatsink.

VOLTAGE REGULATOR

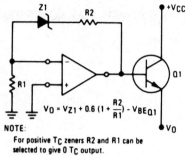

$$V_O = V_{Z1} + 0.6\left(1 + \frac{R2}{R1}\right) - V_{BEQ1}$$

NOTE:

For positive T_C zeners R2 and R1 can be selected to give 0 T_C output.

MOTOROLA   *Fig. 2-81*

ZENER DIODE REGULATOR

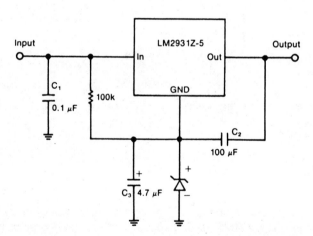

ELECTRONIC DESIGN   *Fig. 2-82*

A zener diode in the ground lead of a fixed pnp regulator varies the voltage output of that device without a significant sacrifice in regulation. The technique also allows the regulator to operate with output voltages beyond its rated limit.

12- to 14-V REGULATED 3-A POWER SUPPLY

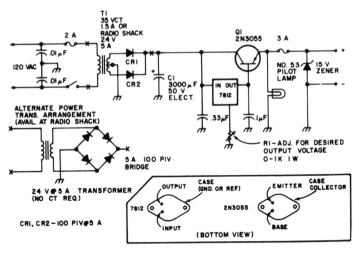

73 AMATEUR RADIO

Fig. 2-83

dc-TO-dc SMPS VARIABLE (18 TO 30 V OUT AT 0.2 A)

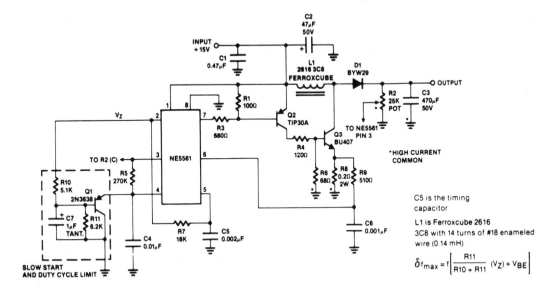

C5 is the timing capacitor

L1 is Ferroxcube 2616 3C8 with 14 turns of #18 enameled wire (0.14 mH)

$$\delta f_{max} = f \left| \frac{R11}{R10 + R11} (V_Z) + V_{BE} \right|$$

SIGNETICS

Fig. 2-84

SCR PREREGULATOR FITS ANY POWER SUPPLY

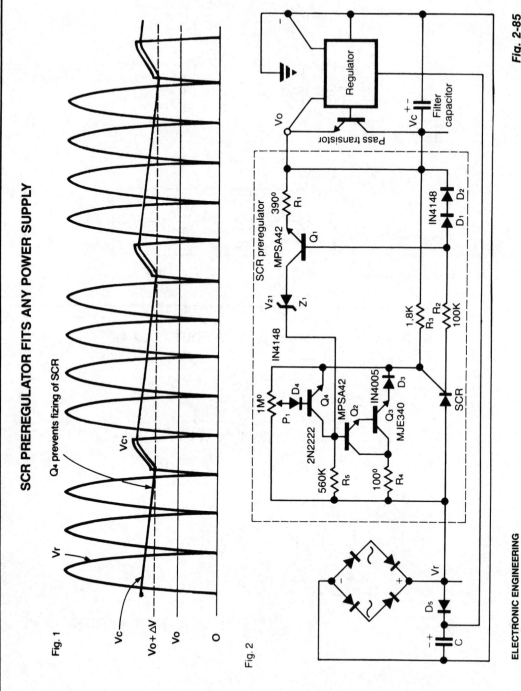

Fig. 1

Fig. 2

Fig. 2-85

ELECTRONIC ENGINEERING

This SCR preregulator keeps the filter capacitor V_c, in a variable-output power supply a few volts above the output voltage, V_o. The benefits include: less heat dissipated by the pass transistor and therefore a smaller heatsink, cooler operation, and higher efficiency—especially at low output voltages.

Q1, R1, R2, D1 and D2 form a constant-current source for zener Z1 so that the contribution to the output current is always a few mA (2 to 3 mA).

The Darlington pair (Q2, Q3) keeps the SCR off. The voltage, V_c, decreases until $V_c = V_o = V$, at which point the Darlington pair fires the SCR, charging the filter capacitor to a higher voltage (V_c^1) in less than half the period of the input voltage. The component values shown are for a 0- to 250-V 3-A power supply.

OFF-LINE FLYBACK REGULATOR

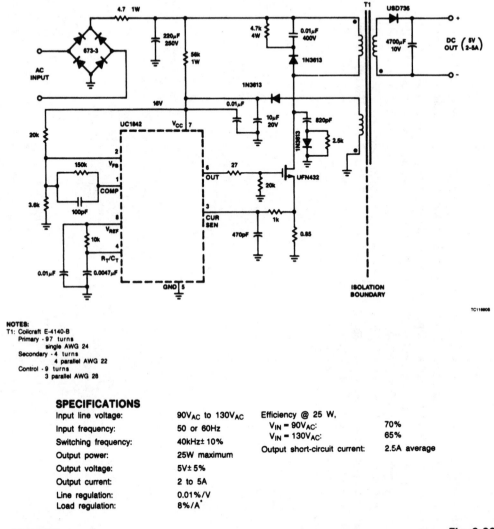

NOTES:
T1: Coilcraft E-4140-B
  Primary - 97 turns
      single AWG 24
  Secondary - 4 turns
      4 parallel AWG 22
  Control - 9 turns
      3 parallel AWG 28

SPECIFICATIONS

Input line voltage:	$90V_{AC}$ to $130V_{AC}$
Input frequency:	50 or 60Hz
Switching frequency:	40kHz± 10%
Output power:	25W maximum
Output voltage:	5V± 5%
Output current:	2 to 5A
Line regulation:	0.01%/V
Load regulation:	8%/A*

Efficiency @ 25 W,
V_{IN} = $90V_{AC}$:	70%
V_{IN} = $130V_{AC}$:	65%
Output short-circuit current:	2.5A average

SIGNETICS

Fig. 2-86

This circuit uses a low-cost feedback scheme in which the dc voltage developed from the primary-side control winding is sensed by the UC1842 error amplifier. Load regulation is therefore dependent on the coupling between secondary and control windings, and on transformer leakage inductance. For applications that require better load regulation, a UC1901 Isolated Feedback Generator can be used to directly sense the output voltage.

500-kHz SWITCHING INVERTER FOR 12-V SYSTEMS

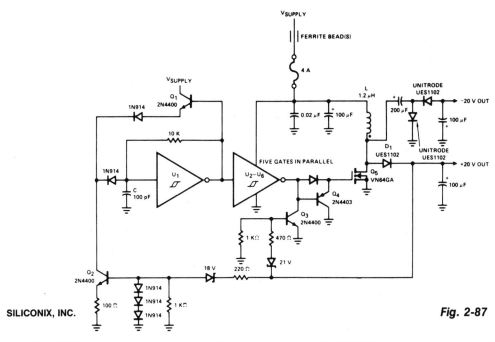

SILICONIX, INC.

Fig. 2-87

This PWM-control circuit provides the control pulse to the DMOS power switch in the flyback circuit. The output of the PWM is a pulse whose width is proportional to the input control voltage and whose repetition rate is determined by an external clock signal. To provide the control input to the PWM and to prevent the output voltage from soaring or sagging as the load changes the error amplifier and reference voltage complete the design. They act as the feedback loop in this control circuit, much like that of a servo control system.

10-A REGULATOR WITH CURRENT AND THERMAL PROTECTION

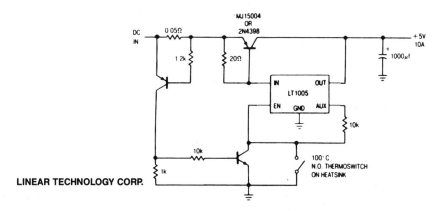

LINEAR TECHNOLOGY CORP.

Fig. 2-88

BIPOLAR POWER SUPPLY FOR BATTERY INSTRUMENTS

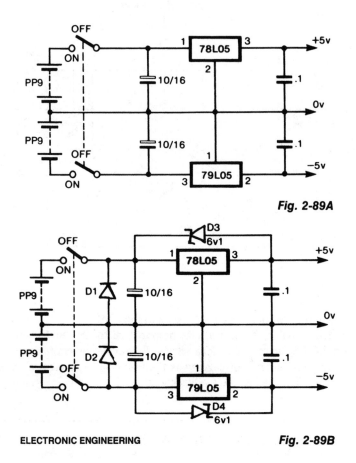

Fig. 2-89A

ELECTRONIC ENGINEERING

Fig. 2-89B

To generate regulated ± 5-V supplies from a pair of dry batteries, the circuit of Fig. 2-89A is commonly used. In order to give protection from inadvertent reverse connection of a battery, a diode in series with each battery would produce an unacceptable voltage drop. The more effective approach is to fit diodes D1 and D2 (Fig. 2-89B) in parallel with each battery.

When the supply is switched off, there is the risk of a reverse bias being applied across the regulators, if significant inductance or capacitance is in the load circuit. Diodes across the regulators prevent damage. When the power supply is switched on, the two switches do not act in unison. Probably, one or the other regulators will be latched hard off by the other. To prevent this, D3 and D4 are zener diodes so that ± 5-V rails are pulled up by the batteries until the regulators establish the correct levels.

POWER SUPPLY FOR 25-W ARC LAMP

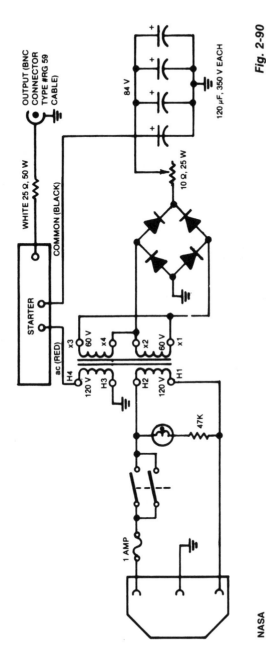

Fig. 2-90

NASA

Dual-voltage circuitry both strikes and maintains the arc. The lamps require a starting voltage in excess of 1,000 volts. Once stabilized, the voltage drop across the lamp is near 20 volts. The power supply consists of two main sections. The first section, the low-voltage power supply, is an 84-V direct-current supply. This supply powers the stabilized arc. Current is limited by the 10-Ω adjustable and 25-Ω fixed resistance. The second section, the high-voltage starter circuit, is a Cockroft-Walton voltage multiplier. With no load, the output voltage is 2,036 V. However, when the arc is established, the heavy current drain maintains a forward bias on all of the diodes, and the circuit becomes a straight path with a voltage drop of 7.2 V. The small value of the capacitors used in the multiplier guarantees that the diodes will be forward-biased once the arc is established.

POWER-SWITCHING CIRCUIT

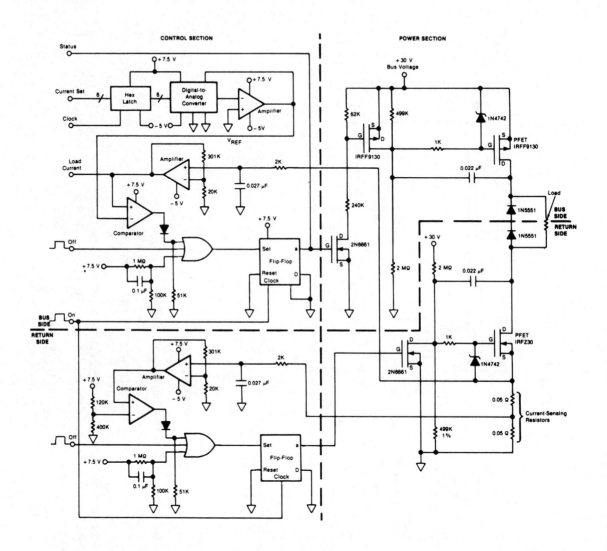

NASA

Fig. 2-91

This circuit provides on/off switching, soft starting, current monitoring, current tripping, and protection against overcurrent for a 30-Vdc power supply at normal load currents up to 2 A. The switch is turned on by an ''on'' command pulse; it is turned off by an ''off'' command pulse. An overcurrent trip can also be set on the bus side by a 6-digit binary signal, which is converted to an analog voltage and compared with the amplified voltage developed across a load-current-sensing resistor. Resistor/capacitor combinations (2 kΩ/0.027 μF) at the inputs of the current-sensing amplifiers act as low-pass filters: this introduces a few hundred μs of delay in the response to overcurrent, thereby providing some immunity to noise. The 0.022-μF capacitors connected to the drain terminals of the PFETs provide a Miller effect, which reduces the rate of change of the drain voltage and therefore the rate of rise of current at turn-on. The soft-turn-on time depends upon the load impedance and is typically 100 to 200 ms.

100-V/0.25-A SWITCH MODE CONVERTER

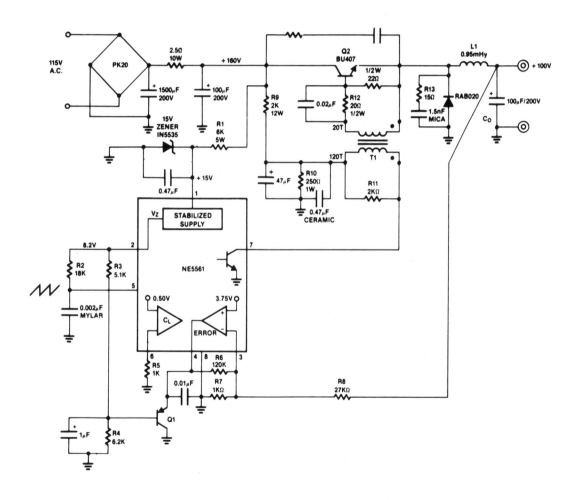

SIGNETICS

Fig. 2-92

RADIATION-HARDENED 125-A LINEAR REGULATOR

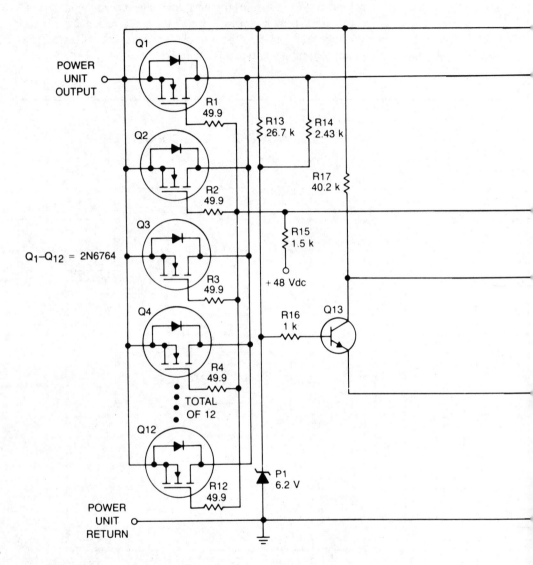

MOTOROLA

Intended for extreme-temperature radiation-hardened environments, this linear supply is capable of supplying 28 Vdc a 125 A from an ac-driven power unit.

In operation, power-supply output voltage is sensed by the voltage divider, which consists of R24 to R28 and is fed to one input of a discrete differential amplifier (composed of Q13 through Q16). The other

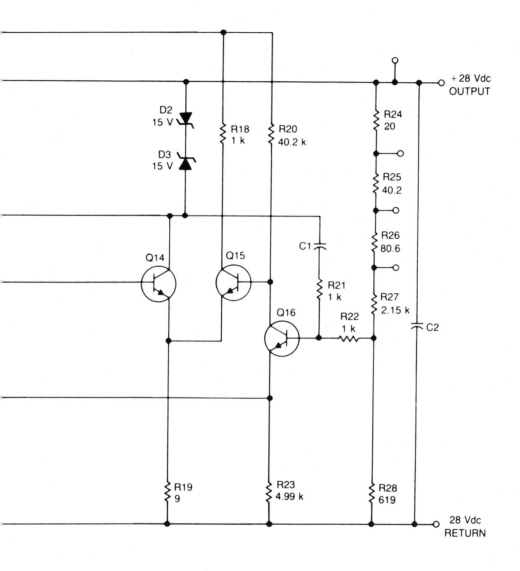

Fig. 2-93

input of the amplifier is connected to a radiation-hardened zener diode, D1. Local feedback (using R21 and C1) produces gain to phase shift that is independent of individual component parameters, which provide stable operation into the required loads.

SUPPLY VOLTAGE SPLITTER

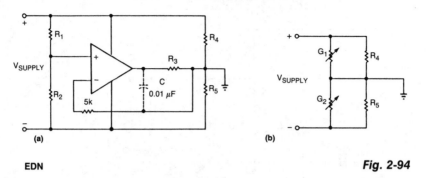

EDN

Fig. 2-94

This simple circuit can convert a single supply voltage, such as a battery, into a bipolar supply. Sense resistors R1 and R2 establish relative magnitudes for the resulting positive and negative voltages. Their rail-to-rail value, of course, equals V_{SUPPLY}. R4 and R5 represent the load impedances. For example, equal-value sense resistors produce $1/2$ V_{SUPPLY} across each of the load resistors, R4 and R5. The op amp maintains these equal voltages by sinking or sourcing current through R3; the op amp's action is equivalent to that of variable conductances G1 and G2 in shunt with each load resistor. Choose a value for R3 so that the largest voltage across it, the greatest load-current mismatch, won't exceed the op amp's output-voltage capability for the application. You can add a buffer amplifier at the op amp's output to provide greater load currents. If you need bypass capacitors across the load resistors as well, connect a capacitor (dashed lines) to ensure that the amplifier remains stable.

3- TO 5-V REGULATED OUTPUT CONVERTER

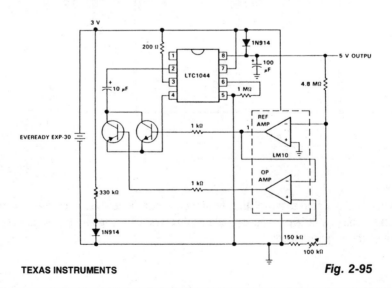

TEXAS INSTRUMENTS

Fig. 2-95

MEMORY-SAVE ON POWER-DOWN

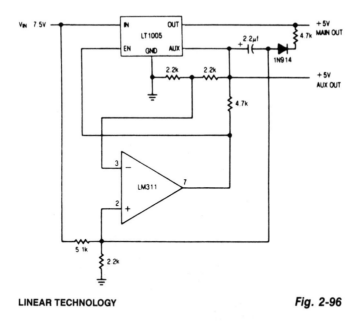

LINEAR TECHNOLOGY

Fig. 2-96

The auxiliary output powers the memory; the main output powers the system and is connected to the memory-store pin. When power goes down, the main output goes low and commands the memory to store. The auxiliary output then drops out.

100-Vrms VOLTAGE REGULATOR

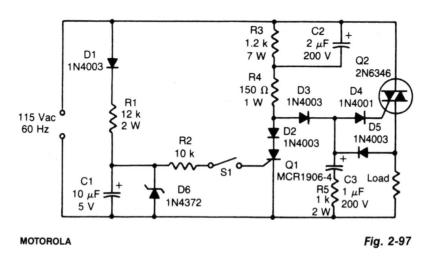

MOTOROLA

Fig. 2-97

3

Power Supplies—High Voltage

The sources of the following circuits are contained in the Sources section, which begins on page 125. The figure number in the box of each circuit correlates to the source entry in the Sources section.

LOW-COST ULTRA-HIGH-VOLTAGE GENERATOR

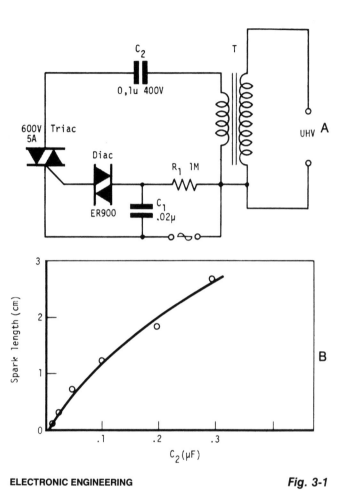

ELECTRONIC ENGINEERING

Fig. 3-1

By repetitively charging and discharging a capacitor through the primary of an induction coil with a high voltage, an ultra-high emf is induced in the secondary. Switching is performed by the triac, triggered by the disc capacitor at times set by C1 and R1. With a 12-V car ignition coil, for example, the length of spark obtained is 12 mm of air for $C_2 = 0.1$ μF. If the dielectric strength in air is assumed to be 3 kV/mm, this spark-gap length corresponds to 36 kV. From the curve shown in Fig. B, care must be taken to keep the value of C2 below 1 μF because the coil is liable to be seriously damaged at higher capacitance than this value. Power consumption is only about one watt.

SIMPLE HIGH-VOLTAGE SUPPLY

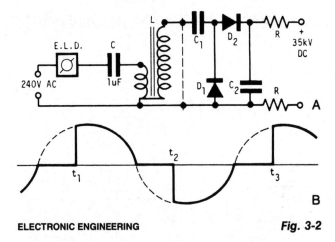

ELECTRONIC ENGINEERING

Fig. 3-2

A light dimmer, a 1-μF capacitor and a 12-V car ignition coil form the simple line-powered HV generator. The current in the dimmer is shown in Fig. B. At times t_1, t_2, . . . , set by the dimmer switch, the inner triac of the dimmer switches on, and a very high and very fast current pulse charges the capacitor through the primary of the induction coil. Then, at a rate of 120 times per second for a 60-Hz line, a very high voltage pulse appears at the secondary of the coil. To obtain an HV dc output, use a voltage doubler. D1 and D2 are selenium rectifiers (TV 18 Siemens or ITT) used for the supply of television sets. High-value output shock-protection resistors, R, are recommended when suitable.

HIGH-VOLTAGE GEIGER-COUNTER SUPPLY

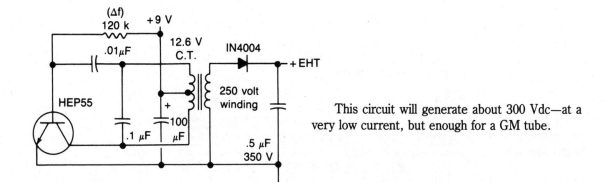

This circuit will generate about 300 Vdc—at a very low current, but enough for a GM tube.

POPULAR ELECTRONICS

Fig. 3-3

ARC-JET POWER SUPPLY AND STARTING CIRCUIT

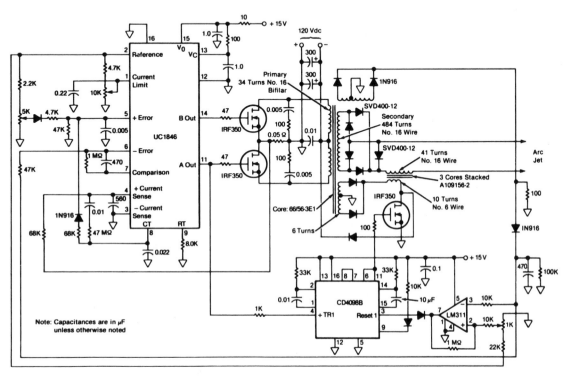

Fig. 3-4

This circuit for starting arc jets and controlling them in steady operation is capable of high power efficiency and can be constructed in a lightweight form. The design comprises a pulse-width-modulated power converter, which is configured in a closed control loop for fast current control. The series averaging inductor maintains nearly constant current during rapid voltage changes, and thereby allows time for the fast-response regulator to adjust its pulse width to accommodate load-voltage changes. The output averaging inductor doubles as the high-voltage pulse transformer for ignition. The starting circuit operates according to the same principle as that of an automobile ignition coil. When the current is interrupted by a transistor switch, the inductor magnetic field collapses, and a high-voltage pulse is produced. The pulse is initiated every 0.25 second until arc current is detected, then the pulser is automatically turned off.

PREREGULATED HIGH-VOLTAGE SUPPLY

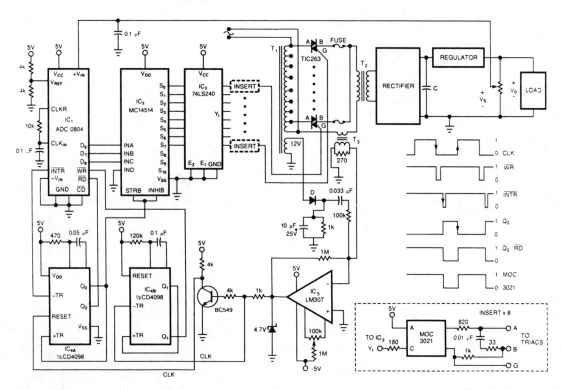

Fig. 3-5

One of the control circuit's triacs selects the tap on main transformer T1, which provides the proper, preregulated voltage to the secondary regulator. T2 and its associated components comprise the secondary regulator.

The ADC 0804, IC1, digitizes a voltage-feedback signal from the secondary regulator's output. The MC1415 demultiplexer, IC2, decodes the digitizer's output. IC2, in turn, drives T1's optoisolated triacs via the 74LS240 driver chip, IC3, and associated optoisolators.

Transformer T3 samples the circuit's current output. The auxiliary, 12 V winding on T1 ensures no-load starting. The combination of op amp IC5 and the inverting transistor, Q1, square this current signal. The output of Q1 is the CLK signal, which triggers one-half of the one shot, IC4A, to begin the circuit's A/D conversion. The one shots' periods are set to time out within $1/2$ cycle of the ac input.

Upon completion of its A/D conversion, IC1's INTR output triggers the other half of the one shot, IC4B, which enables the converter's data outputs. The rising edge of the CLK signal resets the one shot and latches the new conversion value into IC2. The latch, associated driver, and optoisolator trigger a selected triac according to the latest value of the voltage-feedback signal, V_o.

HIGH-VOLTAGE BUCKING REGULATOR

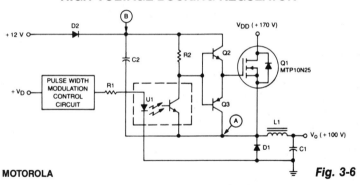

MOTOROLA

Fig. 3-6

This circuit is basically the classic bucking regulator, except it uses a TMOS N-channel power FET for the chopper and creates its own supply for the gate control.

The unique aspect of this circuit is how it generates a separate supply for the gate circuit, which must be greater than V_{DD}. When power is applied, C2 charges, through D2, to +12 V. At this time, Q1 is off and the voltage at point A is just below zero. When the pulse-modulated signal is applied, the optoisolator transistors, Q2 and Q3, supply a signal to Q1 that turns it on. The voltage at point A then goes to V_{DD}, C2 back-biases D2, and the voltage at point B becomes 12 V above V_{DD}.

After Q1 is turned on, current starts to flow through L1 into C1, increasing until Q1 turns off. The current still wants to flow through L1, so the voltage at point A moves toward negative infinity, but is clamped by D1 to just below zero. Current flows less and less into C1, until Q1 turns on again. Q2 and Q3 drive Q1's gate between the voltages at point A and B, which is always a 12-V swing, so V_{GS} max. is never exceeded. For proper operation, the 12-V supply has to be established before the pulse-width modulator signal is applied.

HIGH-VOLTAGE dc GENERATOR

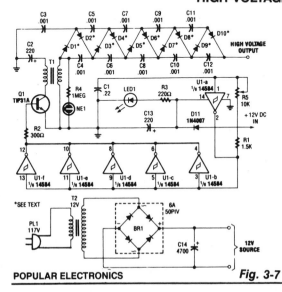

This circuit is fed from a 12-Vdc power supply. The input to the circuit is then amplified to provide a 10,000-Vdc output. The output of the up-converter is then fed into a 10 stage, high-voltage multiplier to produce an output of 10,000 Vdc.

POPULAR ELECTRONICS

Fig. 3-7

BATTERY-POWERED HIGH-VOLTAGE GENERATOR

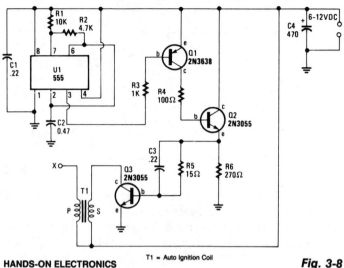

HANDS-ON ELECTRONICS

T1 = Auto Ignition Coil

Fig. 3-8

Output voltage great enough to jump a 1-inch gap can be obtained from a 12-V power source. A 555 timer IC is connected as an astable multivibrator that produces a narrow negative pulse at pin 3. The pulse turns Q1 on for the duration of the time period. The collector of Q1 is direct-coupled to the base of the power transistor Q2, turning it on during the same time period. The emitter of Q2 is direct-coupled through current limiting resistor R5 to the base of the power transistor. Q3 switches on, producing a minimum resistance between the collector and emitter. The high-current pulse going through the primary of high-voltage transformer T1 generates a very high pulse voltage at its secondary output terminal (labeled X). The pulse frequency is determined by the values of R1, R2, and C2. The values given in the parts list were chosen to give the best possible performance when an auto-ignition coil is used for T1.

OPTOISOLATED HIGH-VOLTAGE DRIVER

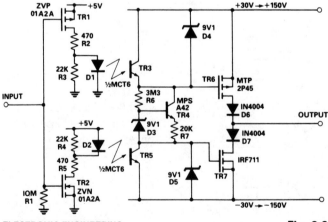

ELECTRONIC ENGINEERING

Fig. 3-9

OPTOISOLATED HIGH-VOLTAGE DRIVER (cont.)

This circuit takes as an input a signal from a 5-V CMOS logic circuit and outputs a high voltage of the same polarity. The high-voltage supply can be varied from ±30 V to ±150 V without the need to change circuit components. The input voltage is applied to the gates of transistors TR1 and TR2.

TR3 is optically coupled to D1 as is TR5 to D2. R5 limits the current through D2, while R3 and R4 reduce the effects of leakage current. The light transmitted by D1 turns TR3 on and discharges the gatesource capacitance of TR6, which turns TR6 off. At the same time, TR5 is off and a constant current produced by R6, R7, D3, and TR4 charges the gate-sourced capacitance of TR7, thus turning TR7 on. With TR7 on and TR6 off, the output is pulled close to the lower supply rail. When the input is high, TR1 is off and TR2 is on. Therefore, D2 conducts, which turns on TR5. With TR3 off and TR5 on, TR6 turns on and TR7 off. The output is pulled towards the higher supply rail.

SIMPLE HIGH-VOLTAGE SUPPLY

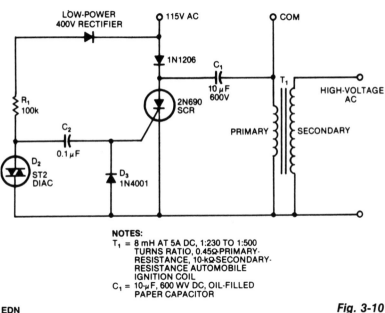

NOTES:
T₁ = 8 mH AT 5A DC, 1:230 TO 1:500
TURNS RATIO, 0.45Ω PRIMARY-
RESISTANCE, 10-kΩ SECONDARY-
RESISTANCE AUTOMOBILE
IGNITION COIL
C₁ = 10-μF, 600 WV DC, OIL-FILLED
PAPER CAPACITOR

EDN   *Fig. 3-10*

This circuit can generate high-voltage pulses with an inexpensive auto ignition coil. Add a rectifier on the output and the circuit produces high-voltage dc. The circuit's input is 115 Vac. During the inputs positive half cycle, energy is stored in capacitor C1, which is charged via diode D1 and the primary winding of transformer T1, the coil. The SCR and its trigger circuitry are inactive during this period. During the input's negative half cycle, energy is stored in capacitor C2 until diac D2 reaches its trigger voltage, whereupon D2 conducts abruptly and C2 releases its energy into the SCR's gate. The SCR then discharges C1 into the transformer's primary and ceases to conduct. This store-and-release cycle repeats on the line's positive and negative half cycles, producing high-voltage pulses at the transformer's secondary.

HIGH-VOLTAGE INVERTER

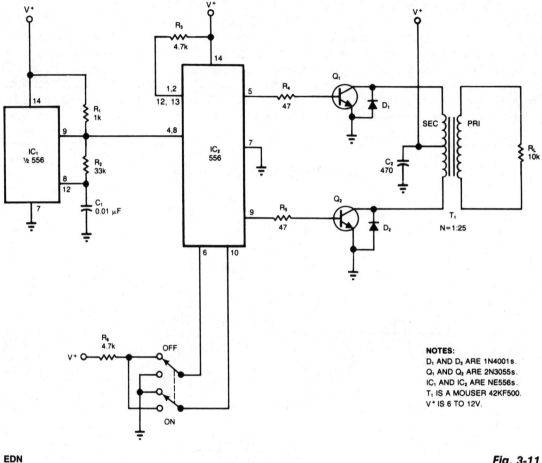

NOTES:
D₁ AND D₂ ARE 1N4001s.
Q₁ AND Q₂ ARE 2N3055s.
IC₁ AND IC₂ ARE NE556s.
T₁ IS A MOUSER 42KF500.
V⁺ IS 6 TO 12V.

EDN

Fig. 3-11

The circuit converts a dc voltage (V⁺) to a high-amplitude square wave in the audio-frequency range. The dual timer, IC2, provides an inexpensive alternative to the traditional transformer for providing complementary base drive to the power transistors, Q1 and Q2. You can convert a 6- to 12-V battery output, for example, to an ac amplitude, which is limited primarily by the power rating of transformer T1. Connect timer IC1 as an oscillator to provide a symmetrical square-wave drive to both inputs of IC2. The timing components, R2 and C1, produce a 2.2-kHz output frequency. By connecting half of IC2 in the inverting mode and the other half in noninverting mode, the timer's outputs alternately drive the two transistors. You can operate the audio-output transformer, T1, as a step-up transformer by connecting it backwards— using the output winding as an input. The transformer delivers an output voltage across R_L of $4 \times N \times V^+ V$ pk-pk, where N is the transformer turns ratio. For this circuit, the output swing is $100 \times V^+ V$ pk-pk.

HIGH-VOLTAGE REGULATOR

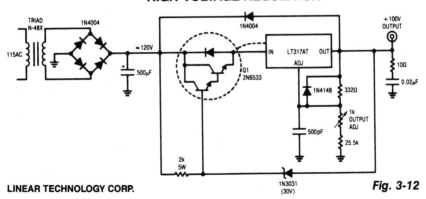

LINEAR TECHNOLOGY CORP.   *Fig. 3-12*

The regulator delivers 100 V at 100 mA and withstands shorts to ground. Even at 100-V output, the LT317A functions in the normal mode, maintaining 1.2 V between its output and adjustment pin. Under these conditions, the 30-V zener is off and Q1 conducts. When an output short occurs, the zener conducts, forcing Q1's base to 30 V. This causes Q1's emitter to clamp 2 V_{BE}s below V_Z, well within the V_{IN}-V_{OUT} rating of the regulator. Under these conditions, Q1, a high-voltage device, sustains 90 V-V_{CE} at whatever current the transformer specified saturates at 130 mA, while Q1 safely dissipates 12 W. If Q1 and the LT317A are thermally coupled, the regulator will soon go into thermal shutdown and oscillation will commence. This action will continue, protecting the load and the regulator as long as the output remains shorted. The 500-pF capacitor and the 10 Ω/0.02 μF damper aid transient response and the diodes provide safe discharge paths for the capacitors.

CAPACITOR-DISCHARGE HIGH-VOLTAGE GENERATOR

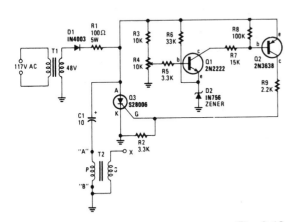

HANDS-ON ELECTRONICS   *Fig. 3-13*

Stepdown transformer T1 drops the incoming line voltage to approximately 48 Vac which is rectified by diode D1; the resultant dc charges capacitor C1—through current limiting resistor R1—to a voltage level preset by R4. When the voltage on R4's wiper reaches about 8.6 V, Q1 begins to turn on, drawing current through R7 and the base-emitter junction of Q2. Q2 turns on and supplies a positive voltage to the gate of silicon-controlled rectifier Q3. The positive gate voltage causes Q3 to conduct, thereby discharging C1 through the primary winding of step-up transformer T2, which results in a high-voltage arc at output terminal X. The voltage developed at T2's output is determined by the value of C1, the voltage across C1, and the turns ratio of transformer T2. The frequency or pulse rate of the high voltage is determined by the resistance of T1's primary and secondary windings, the value of R1, and the value of C1. The lower the value of each item, the higher the output pulse rate; the peak output voltage will only remain unchanged if C1's value remains unchanged.

REMOTELY ADJUSTABLE SOLID-STATE HIGH-VOLTAGE SUPPLY

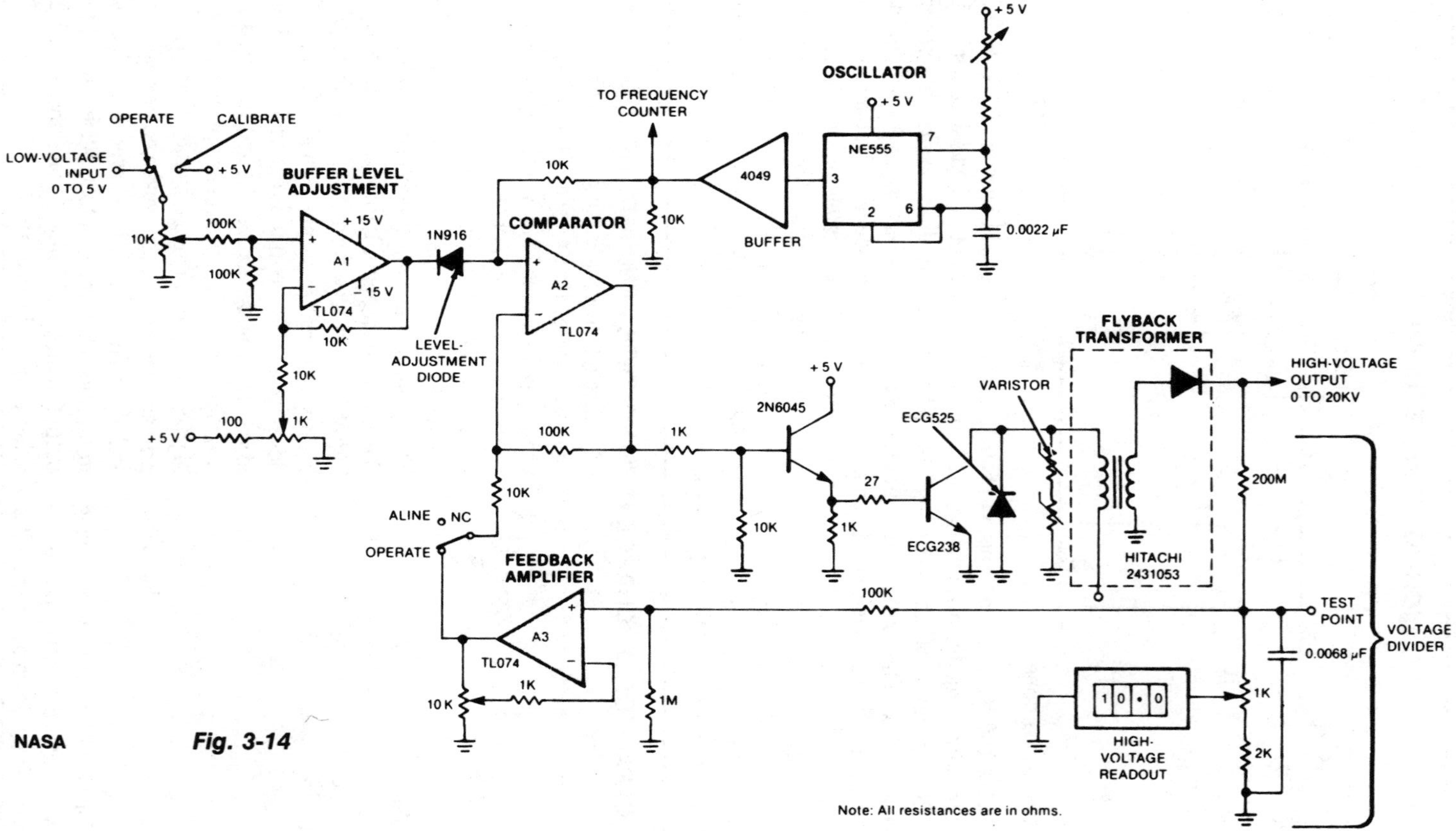

Fig. 3-14

NASA

Note: All resistances are in ohms.

The output voltage changes approximately linearly up to 20 kV as the input voltage is varied from 0 to 5 V. The oscillator is tuned by a 5-kΩ potentiometer to peak the output voltage at the frequency of maximum transformer response between 45 and 55 kHz. The feedback voltage is applied through a 100-kΩ resistor, an op amp, and a comparator to a high-voltage amplifier. A diode and varistors on the primary side of the transformer protect the output transistor. The transformer is a flyback-type used in color-television sets. A feedback loop balances between the high-voltage output and the low-voltage input.

POWER CONVERTER

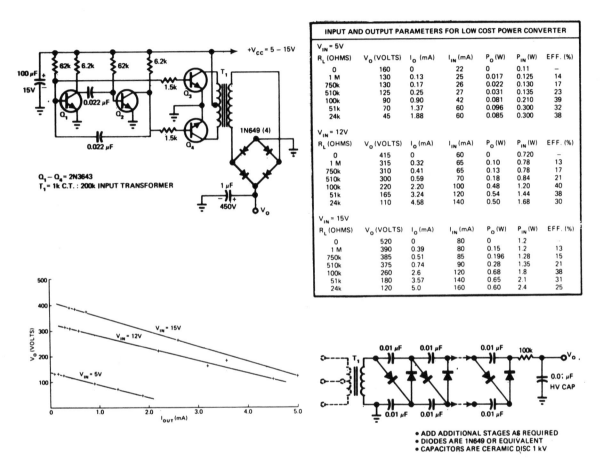

INPUT AND OUTPUT PARAMETERS FOR LOW COST POWER CONVERTER						
V_{IN} = 5V						
R_L (OHMS)	V_O (VOLTS)	I_O (mA)	I_{IN} (mA)	P_O (W)	P_{IN} (W)	EFF. (%)
0	160	0	22	0	0.11	–
1 M	130	0.13	25	0.017	0.125	14
750k	130	0.17	26	0.022	0.130	17
510k	125	0.25	27	0.031	0.135	23
100k	90	0.90	42	0.081	0.210	39
51k	70	1.37	60	0.096	0.300	32
24k	45	1.88	60	0.085	0.300	38
V_{IN} = 12V						
R_L (OHMS)	V_O (VOLTS)	I_O (mA)	I_{IN} (mA)	P_O (W)	P_{IN} (W)	EFF. (%)
0	415	0	60	0	0.720	–
1 M	315	0.32	65	0.10	0.78	13
750k	310	0.41	65	0.13	0.78	17
510k	300	0.59	70	0.18	0.84	21
100k	220	2.20	100	0.48	1.20	40
51k	165	3.24	120	0.54	1.44	38
24k	110	4.58	140	0.50	1.68	30
V_{IN} = 15V						
R_L (OHMS)	V_O (VOLTS)	I_O (mA)	I_{IN} (mA)	P_O (W)	P_{IN} (W)	EFF. (%)
0	520	0	80	0	1.2	–
1 M	390	0.39	80	0.15	1.2	13
750k	385	0.51	85	0.196	1.28	15
510k	375	0.74	90	0.28	1.35	21
100k	260	2.6	120	0.68	1.8	38
51k	180	3.57	140	0.65	2.1	31
24k	120	5.0	160	0.60	2.4	25

- ADD ADDITIONAL STAGES AS REQUIRED
- DIODES ARE 1N649 OR EQUIVALENT
- CAPACITORS ARE CERAMIC DISC 1 kV

EDN

Fig. 3-15

This circuit consists of an astable multivibrator driving a push-pull pair of transistors into the transformer primary. The multivibrator frequency should equal around 1 or 2 kHz. For higher dc voltages, voltage multipliers on the secondary circuit have been used successfully to generate 10 kV from a 40-stage multiplier like the one shown.

400-V 60-W PUSH-PULL POWER SUPPLY

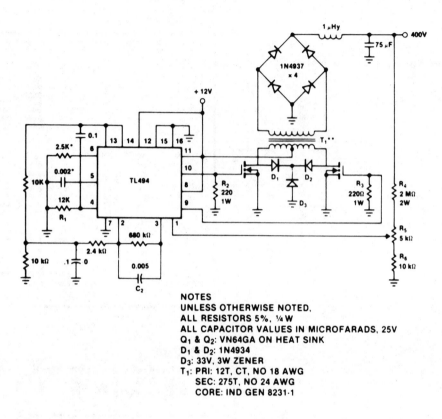

NOTES
UNLESS OTHERWISE NOTED,
ALL RESISTORS 5%, ¼ W
ALL CAPACITOR VALUES IN MICROFARADS, 25V
Q_1 & Q_2: VN64GA ON HEAT SINK
D_1 & D_2: 1N4934
D_3: 33V, 3W ZENER
T_1: PRI: 12T, CT, NO 18 AWG
    SEC: 275T, NO 24 AWG
    CORE: IND GEN 8231-1

SILICONIX, INC.

Fig. 3-16

The design delivers a regulated 400-V 60-W output. The TL494 switching regulator governs the operating frequency and regulates output voltage. R1 and C1 determine switching frequency, which is approximately 0.5RC—100 kHz for the values shown. The TL494 directly drives the FET's gates with a voltage-controlled, pulse-width-modulated signal. After full-wave rectification, the output waveform is filtered by a choke-input arrangement. The 1-μH 75-μF filter accomplishes the job nicely at 100 kHz. A feedback scheme using R4, R5, and R6 provides for output-voltage regulation adjustment, with loop compensation handled by C2. Diodes D1 and D2 provide isolation and steering for the 33-V zener transient clamp, D3. Output regulation is typically 1.25% from no-load to the full 60-W design rating. Regulation is essentially determined by the TL494. Output noise and ripple consists mainly of positive and negative 0.8-V spikes that occur when the output stage switches.

HV REGULATOR WITH FOLDBACK CURRENT LIMITING

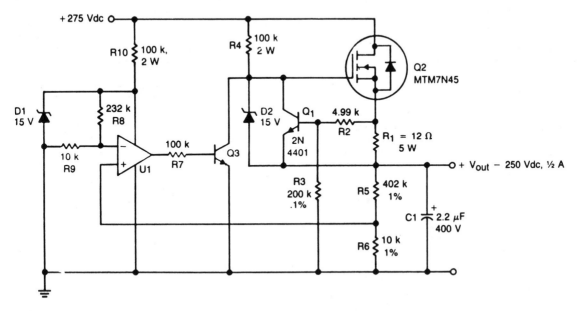

MOTOROLA

Fig. 3-17

A TMOS MTM7N45 (Q2) is used as a series pass element in a linear high-voltage supply that accepts +275-V unregulated and produces 250 V regulated with foldback current limiting.

A 15-V zener, D1, provides the dc reference for operational amplifier U1, whose other input is obtained from a fraction of the output voltage. U1 drives Q3, which drives the gate of Q2. Foldback current limiting is achieved by R1, R2, R3, R4, Q1, and D2. The formula to establish the current "knee" for limiting is:

$$I_{KNEE} = \frac{V_{OUT}(R_2/R_2 + R_3) + 0.5 \text{ V}}{R_1}$$

Short circuit current is:

$$I_{SC} = \frac{0.5 \text{ V}}{R_1}$$

SIMPLE TESLA COIL

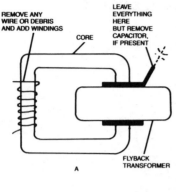

A

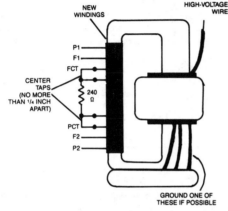

B

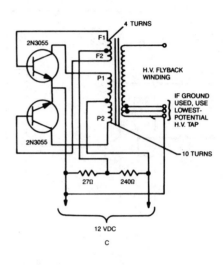

C

Fig. 3-18

The Tesla coil described here can generate 25,000 V. So, even though the output current is low, **be very careful!** The main component is a flyback transformer from a discarded TV.

A new primary winding is needed. Begin by winding 5 turns of #18 wire on the core. Then, twist a loop in the wire, and finish by winding five more turns. Wrap with electrical tape, but leave the loop exposed.

A four-turn winding must be wound over the ten-turn winding that you've just finished. That is done the same way. First wind two turns of #18 wire, then make a loop, and finish by winding two more turns. Again, wrap the new winding with electrical tape, leaving the loop exposed.

When the windings are finished, the two loops shouldn't be more than 1/4-inch apart, but take care that they do not touch. Connect a 240-Ω resistor between the two loops. The modified transformer now should look like the one shown. Connect the transformer as shown. The 27-Ω resistor and two transistors should be mounted on a heatsink and must be insulated from it.

The output of the high-voltage winding should begin to oscillate as soon as the circuit is connected to a 12-Vdc power supply. If it does not, reverse the connections to the base leads of the transistors. In normal operation, you should be able to draw 1-inch sparks from the high-voltage lead using an insulated screwdriver.

TESLA COIL

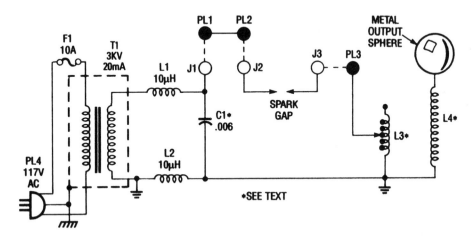

Fig. 3-19

Power is fed to transformer T1, a small neon-sign transformer, which steps the voltage up to about 3,000 Vac. The stepped-up output of T1 is fed through L1 and L2 and across C1, causing the capacitor to charge until enough power is stored in the unit to produce an arc across the spark gap. The spark gap, which momentarily connects C1 and L3 in parallel, determines the amount of current transferred between C1 and L3.

The arcing across the spark gap sends a series of high-voltage pulses through L3, giving a sort of oscillated effect. The energy fed through L3 is transferred to L4 via the magnetic coupling between the two coils. Because of the turn ratio that exists between L3 and L4, an even higher voltage is produced across L4. Coil L4 steps up the voltage, which collects on the top-capacitance sphere. There, it causes an avalanche breakdown of the surrounding air, giving off a luminous discharge.

The rotary spark gap is a simple add-on circuit for the Tesla coil, consisting of a variable dc power supply and a small, 5,000-rpm, dc motor. The circuit allows you to vary the output of the Tesla coil by adjusting the rotating speed of the motor. A rotary gap is far more efficient than a stationary gap, because the stationary gap could cut-out and require readjustment.

HIGH-VOLTAGE SUPPLY

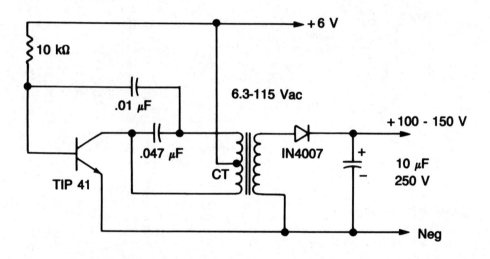

WILLIAM SHEETS

Fig. 3-20

A 6-V battery can provide 100 to 150 Vdc center-tapped at a high internal impedance (not dangerous, though it can inflict an unpleasant jolt). A 6.3-V transformer is connected "in reverse" with a transistor used in a Hartley-oscillator configuration. The frequency of operation can be controlled by varying the value of the 10-kΩ resistor. The 10-μF capacitor must have a working voltage of at least 250 Vdc.

4

Power Supplies—Variable

The sources of the following circuits are contained in the Sources section, which begins on page 125. The figure number in the box of each circuit correlates to the source entry in the Sources section.

ADJUSTABLE REGULATOR (0 to 10 V AT 3 A)

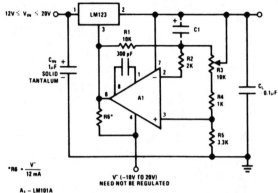

$$*R6 = \frac{V^-}{12\ mA}$$

V⁻ (−10V TO 20V)
NEED NOT BE REGULATED

A₁ − LM101A
C₁ − 2µF OPTIONAL − IMPROVES RIPPLE REJECTION, NOISE, AND TRANSIENT RESPONSE

NATIONAL SEMICONDUCTOR

Fig. 4-1

HIGH-VOLTAGE REGULATOR
(V_{out} = +7 TO 37 V)

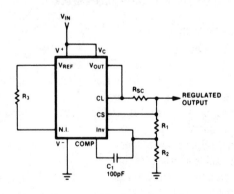

$$V_{OUT} = \left[V_{REF} \times \frac{R_1 + R_2}{R_2} \right]$$

$$R_3 = \frac{R_1\ R_2}{R_1 + R_2} \text{ for minimum temperature drift}$$

R3 may be eliminated for minimum component count

SIGNETICS

Fig. 4-2

LOW-VOLTAGE
REGULATOR (V_{out} = 2 TO 7 V)

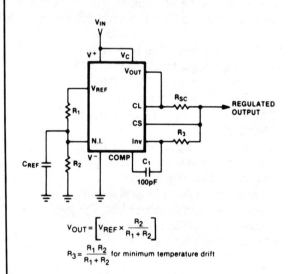

$$V_{OUT} = \left[V_{REF} \times \frac{R_2}{R_1 + R_2} \right]$$

$$R_3 = \frac{R_1\ R_2}{R_1 + R_2} \text{ for minimum temperature drift}$$

SIGNETICS

Fig. 4-3

100-kHz MULTIPLE-OUTPUT SWITCHING POWER SUPPLY

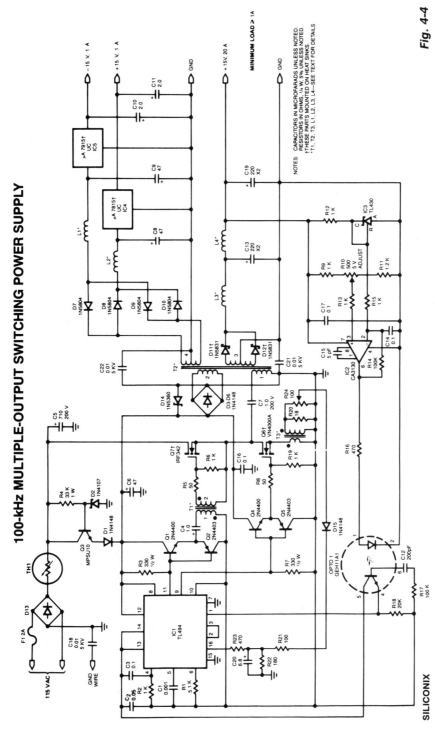

SILICONIX

Fig. 4-4

The power supply uses two VN4000A 400-V MOSPOWER FETs in a half-bridge power switch configuration. Outputs available are +5 V at 20 A and ±15 V (or ±12 V) at 1 A. Since linear three-terminal regulators are used for the low-current outputs, either ±12 V or ±15 V can be made available with a simple change in the transformer secondary windings. A TL494 switching regulator IC provides pulse-width modulation control and drive signals for the power supply. The upper MOSPOWER FET, Q7, in the power switch stage is driven by a simple transformer drive circuit. The lower MOS, Q6, since it is ground referenced, is directly driven from the control IC.

103

MULTIPLE-OUTPUT SWITCHING REGULATOR FOR USE WITH MPUs

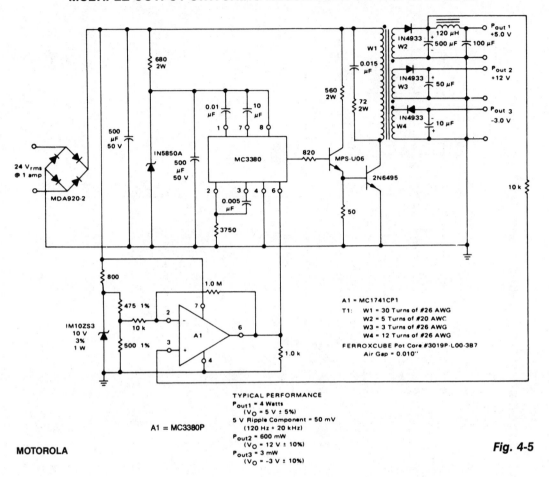

TYPICAL PERFORMANCE

P_{out1} = 4 Watts
   (V_O = 5 V ± 5%)
5 V Ripple Component = 50 mV
   (120 Hz + 20 kHz)
P_{out2} = 600 mW
   (V_O = 12 V ± 10%)
P_{out3} = 3 mW
   (V_O = –3 V ± 10%)

A1 = MC3380P

A1 = MC1741CP1
T1:   W1 = 30 Turns of #26 AWG
     W2 = 5 Turns of #20 AWC
     W3 = 3 Turns of #26 AWG
     W4 = 12 Turns of #26 AWG
FERROXCUBE Pot Core #3019P-L00-387
    Air Gap = 0.010"

MOTOROLA

Fig. 4-5

6.0-A VARIABLE-OUTPUT SWITCHING REGULATOR

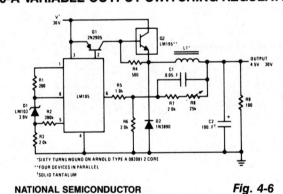

*SIXTY TURNS WOUND ON ARNOLD TYPE A 083081 2 CORE
**FOUR DEVICES IN PARALLEL
†SOLID TANTALUM

NATIONAL SEMICONDUCTOR

Fig. 4-6

POWER PACK FOR BATTERY-POWERED CALCULATORS, RADIOS, OR CASSETTE PLAYERS

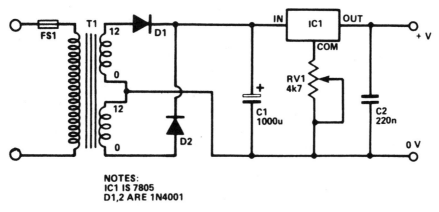

NOTES:
IC1 IS 7805
D1,2 ARE 1N4001

ELECTRONICS TODAY INTERNATIONAL

Fig. 4-7

This circuit produces a regulated output of between 5 and 15 Vdc, adjusted and set by a preset resistor. Current output is up to about 350 mA. An integrated circuit regulates the output voltage. Although this IC (the 7805) is normally used in a fixed-voltage (5 Vdc) supply, it is intended for a variable output voltage.

PRECISION HIGH-VOLTAGE REGULATOR

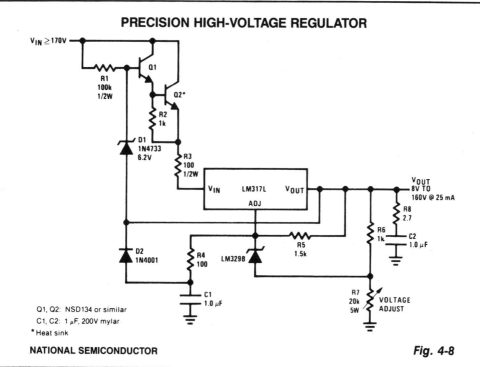

Q1, Q2: NSD134 or similar
C1, C2: 1 μF, 200V mylar
* Heat sink

NATIONAL SEMICONDUCTOR

Fig. 4-8

REMOTE-SHUTDOWN REGULATOR
WITH CURRENT LIMITING
($V_{OUT} = 2$ TO 7 V)

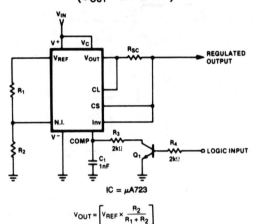

IC = μA723

$$V_{OUT} = \left[V_{REF} \times \frac{R_2}{R_1 + R_2} \right]$$

SIGNETICS   *Fig. 4-9*

0 - TO 30-V REGULATOR

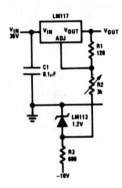

NATIONAL SEMICONDUCTOR   *Fig. 4-11*

0 - TO 22-V REGULATOR

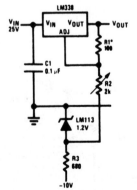

*R1=240Ω, R2 = 5k for LM138 and LM238

NATIONAL SEMICONDUCTOR   *Fig. 4-10*

10-A REGULATOR

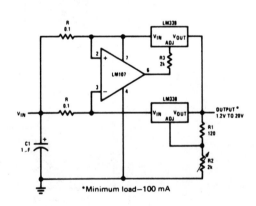

*Minimum load—100 mA

NATIONAL SEMICONDUCTOR   *Fig. 4-12*

12-V TO 9-, 7.5-, or 6-V CONVERTER

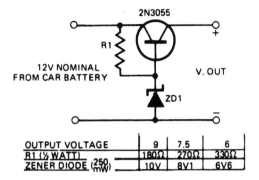

OUTPUT VOLTAGE	9	7.5	6
R1 (½ WATT)	180Ω	270Ω	330Ω
ZENER DIODE (250 mW)	10V	8V1	6V6

ELECTRONICS TODAY INTERNATIONAL *Fig. 4-13*

This circuit enables transistorized items, such as radios, cassettes, and other electrical devices to be operated from a car's electrical supply. The table gives values for resistors and specified diode types for different voltages. If more than one voltage is required, a switching arrangement can be incorporated. For high currents, the transistor should be mounted on a heatsink.

5-A CONSTANT-VOLTAGE/CONSTANT-CURRENT REGULATOR

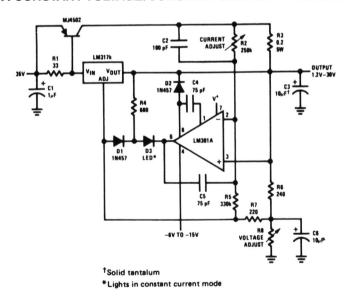

†Solid tantalum
*Lights in constant current mode

NATIONAL SEMICONDUCTOR   *Fig. 4-14*

DUAL-OUTPUT BENCH POWER SUPPLY

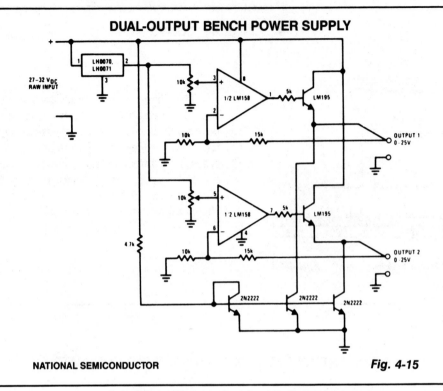

NATIONAL SEMICONDUCTOR

Fig. 4-15

POWER SUPPLY WITH ADJUSTABLE CURRENT LIMIT AND OUTPUT VOLTAGE

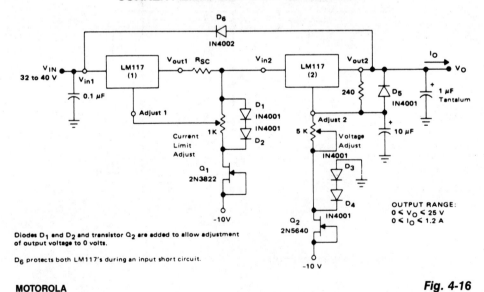

Diodes D_1 and D_2 and transistor Q_2 are added to allow adjustment of output voltage to 0 volts.

D_6 protects both LM117's during an input short circuit.

OUTPUT RANGE:
$0 \leq V_O \leq 25$ V
$0 \leq I_O \leq 1.2$ A

MOTOROLA

Fig. 4-16

SIMPLE SPLIT POWER SUPPLY

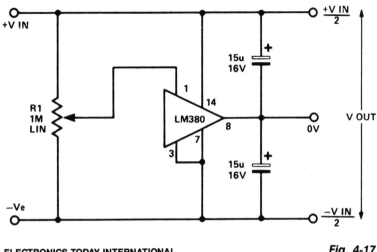

ELECTRONICS TODAY INTERNATIONAL

Fig. 4-17

This circuit utilizes the quasi-complementary output stage of the popular LM380 audio power IC. The device is internally biased so that with no input the output is held midway between the supply rails. R1, which should be initially set to midtravel, is used to nullify any inbalance in the output. Regulation of V_{out} depends upon the circuit feeding the LM380, but positive and negative outputs will track accurately—irrespective of input regulation and unbalanced loads. The free-air dissipation is a little over 1 W, and so extra cooling might be required. The device is fully protected and will go into thermal shutdown if its rated dissipation is exceeded. Current limiting occurs if the output current exceeds 1.3 A. The input voltage should not exceed 20 V.

ADJUSTABLE-OUTPUT REGULATOR

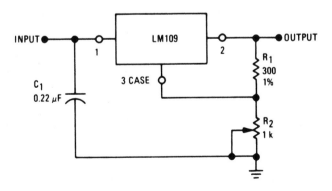

MOTOROLA

Fig. 4-18

REGULATED VOLTAGE DIVIDER

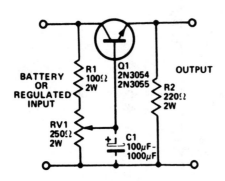

BATTERY
OR
REGULATED
INPUT

R1
100Ω
2W

Q1
2N3054
2N3055

OUTPUT

R2
220Ω
2W

RV1
250Ω
2W

C1
100µF –
1000µF

ELECTRONICS TODAY INTERNATIONAL

Fig. 4-19

ICs requiring 3.6 or 6 V can be run from a battery or a fixed regulated supply of a higher voltage by using the circuit shown. The transistor should be mounted on a heatsink because considerable power will be dissipated by its collector. Additional filtering can be obtained by fitting a capacitor (C1), as shown. The capacitance is effectively multiplied by the gain of the transistor. A ripple of 200 mV (peak to peak) at the input can be reduced to 2 mV in this fashion. Maximum output current depends on the supply rating and transistor type (with heatsink) used.

VARIABLE ZENER DIODE

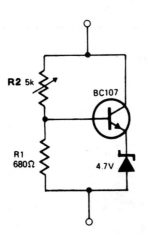

R2 5k

BC107

R1
680Ω

4.7V

ELECTRONICS TODAY INTERNATIONAL

Fig. 4-20

The circuit behaves like a zener diode over a large range of voltages. The current passing through the voltage divider R1/R2 is substantially larger than the transistor base current and is in the region of 8 mA. The stabilizing voltage is adjustable from 5 to 45 V by changing the value of R2. The total current drawn by the circuit is variable from 15 to 50 mA. This value is determined by the maximum dissipation of the zener diode. In the case of a 250-mW device, dissipation is of the order of 50 mA.

110

ADJUSTABLE OUTPUT REGULATOR

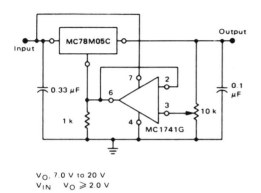

V_O, 7.0 V to 20 V
V_{IN} $V_O \geqslant 2.0$ V

The addition of an operational amplifier allows adjustment to higher or intermediate values, while retaining regulation characteristics. The minimum voltage obtainable with this arrangement is 2.0 V greater than the regulator voltage.

MOTOROLA   *Fig. 4-22*

111

5

Power Supply Monitors

The sources of the following circuits are contained in the Sources section, which begins on page 125. The figure number in the box of each circuit correlates to the source entry in the Sources section.

Power Supply Monitor
Microprocessor Power-Supply Watchdog
Low-Volts Alarm
Power-Supply Balance Indicator
Single-Supply Fault Monitor

POWER SUPPLY MONITOR

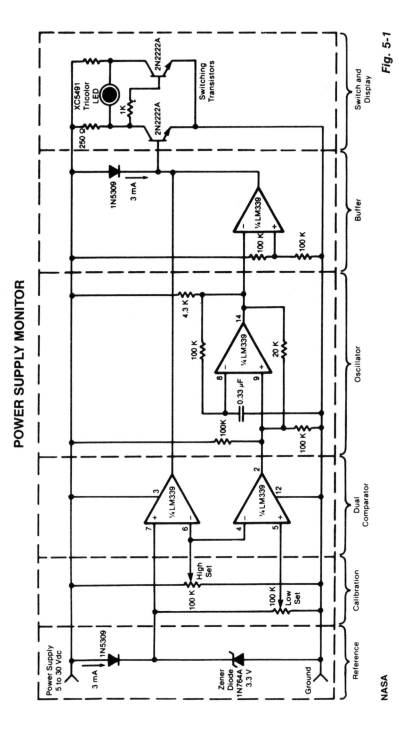

Fig. 5-1

NASA

This circuit uses a tricolor LED display to indicate acceptable and unacceptable output voltages. One sets the upper voltage limit, the other, the lower voltage limit. When the monitored voltage is above the set maximum, the LED display turns red. Yellow turns on for voltages below the set minimum, and green turns on for voltages between the high and the low settings. The circuit does not need a separate power supply. It is powered by the voltage that it monitors. The circuit can be adapted to monitor voltage differences between two power supplies. If the monitored voltages differ by more than a set value, a visual or an audible alarm would warn the operator about the difference. The circuit can also be modified for remote monitoring and the use of a separate power supply.

MICROPROCESSOR POWER-SUPPLY WATCHDOG

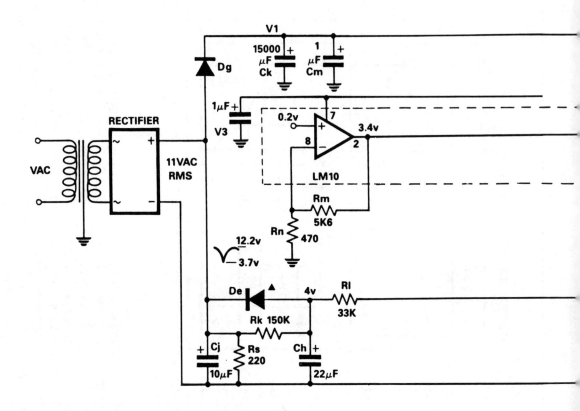

ELECTRONIC ENGINEERING

The circuit monitors the input to the microprocessor 5-V regulated supply for voltage drops and initiates a reset sequence before supply regulation is lost. In operation, the resistor capacitor combination Rs and Cj form a short time-constant smoothing network for the output of the full-wave bridge rectifier. An approximately triangular voltage waveform appears across C and Rs and it is the minimum excursion of this that initiates the reset. Diode Dg prevents charge sharing between capacitors Cj and Ck. Resistors Rn and

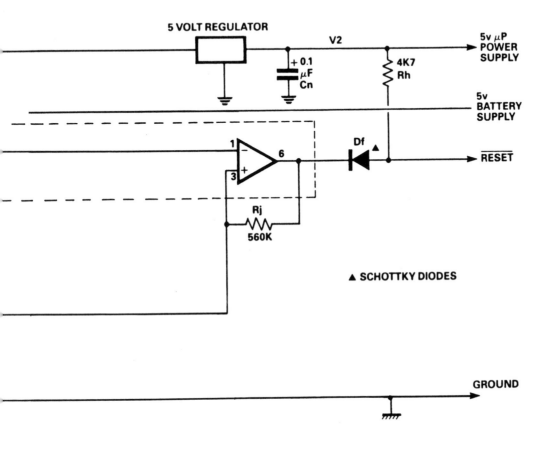

5 VOLT REGULATOR

V2

+ 0.1 μF Cn

4K7 Rh

5v μP POWER SUPPLY

5v BATTERY SUPPLY

Df

$\overline{\text{RESET}}$

Rj
560K

▲ SCHOTTKY DIODES

GROUND

Fig. 5-2

Rm form a feedback network around the voltage reference section of the LM10C, setting a threshold voltage of 3.4 V. The threshold voltage is set at 90% of the minimum voltage of the triangular waveform. When the triangular-wave trough, at the comparator's noninverting input, dips below the threshold, the comparator output is driven low. This presents a reset to the microprocessor. Capacitor Ch is charged slowly through resistor Rk and discharged rapidly through diode De.

LOW-VOLTS ALARM

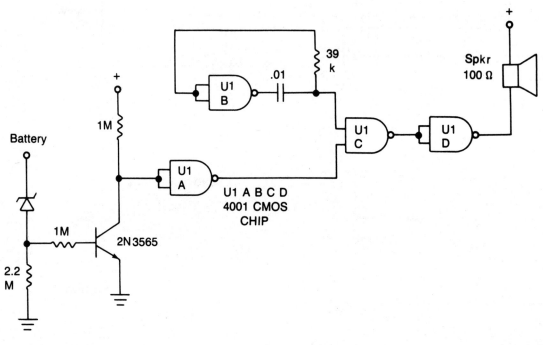

WILLIAM SHEETS

Fig. 5-3

This inexpensive dc supply-voltage monitor sounds a warning when the voltage falls below a preset value. It is ideal for monitoring rechargeable batteries because it draws only a few microamperes when not sounding. The voltage at which the alarm sounds is determined by the zener diode. When the voltage falls below the zener voltage, the alarm sounds. The alarm tone is determined by the RC time constant of the 39-kΩ resistor and 0.01-μf capacitor.

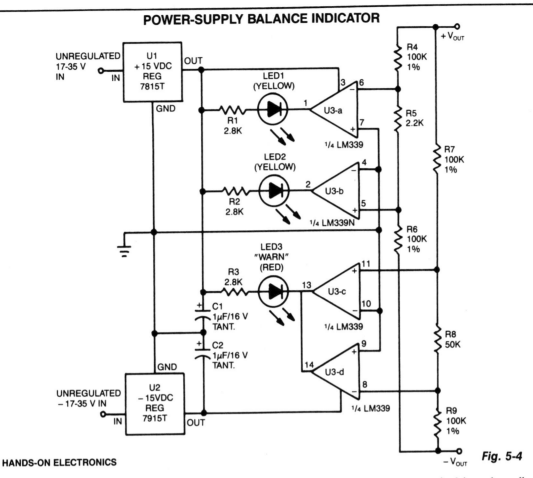

POWER-SUPPLY BALANCE INDICATOR

Fig. 5-4

This circuit uses two comparator pairs from an LM339N quad comparator; one pair drives the yellow positive (+) and negative (−) indicators, the other jointly drives the red warn LED3. The circuit draws its power from the unregulated portion of the power supply. The four comparators get their switching inputs from two parallel resistor-divider strings. Both strings have their ends tied between the power supply's positive and negative output terminals. The first string, consisting of R4, R5, and R6, divides the input voltage in half, with output taps at 0.5%. The other string, made up of R7, R8, and R9, also divides the input voltage in half, with taps at +10%. The 0.5% R4/R5/R6 string drives the two comparators controlling the positive and negative indicators (LED1 and LED2). Their inputs are crossed so that LED2 does not fire until the positive supply is at least 0.5% higher than the negative; the positive indicator does not go off until the negative supply is at least 0.5% higher than the positive—in relative levels. That overlap permits both LEDs to be on when the two supplies are in 1% or better balance. The +10T R7/R8/R9 string drives the other two comparators, which control the warn indicator. If either side of the supply is 10% or more higher than the other, one of the two comparators will switch its output low and light the red LED3— the LM339N has opened-collector outputs, allowing such wired OR connections. The inputs are not crossed, as with the other comparator pair, so there is a band in the middle where neither comparator's output is low and the LED remains off.

SINGLE-SUPPLY FAULT MONITOR

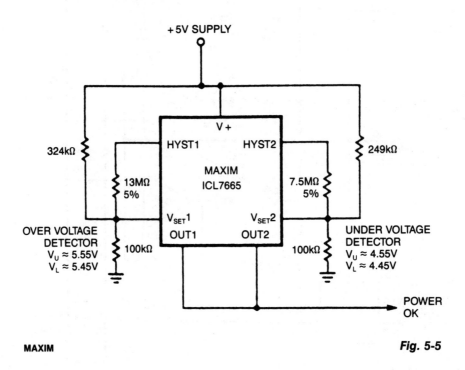

MAXIM

Fig. 5-5

This circuit shows a typical over/under-voltage fault monitor for a single supply. The upper trip points, controlling OUT 1, are centered on 5.5 V with 100 mV of hysteresis ($V_U = 5.55$ V, $V_L = 5.45$ V); and the lower trip points, controlling OUT 2, are centered on 4.5 V, also with 100 mV of hysteresis. OUT 1 and OUT 2 are connected together in a wired OR configuration to generate a *power OK* signal.

6

Power Supply Protection Circuits

The sources of the following circuits are contained in the Sources section, which begins on page 125. The figure number in the box of each circuit correlates to the source entry in the Sources section.

Simple Crowbar
Fast-Acting Power-Supply Protector
5-V Crowbar
Overvoltage Protection with Automatic Reset
Overvoltage Protection for Logic
Overvoltage Protection Circuit (SCR Crowbar)
Power-Supply Protection Circuit

SIMPLE CROWBAR

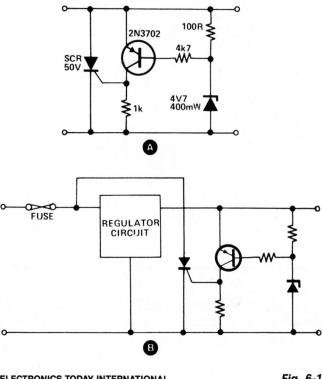

ELECTRONICS TODAY INTERNATIONAL

Fig. 6-1

   These circuits provide overvoltage protection in case of voltage regulator failure or application of an external voltage. Intended to be used with a supply offering some form of short-circuit protection, either foldback, current limiting, or a simple fuse. The most likely application is a 5-V logic supply, because TTL is easily damaged by excess voltage. The values chosen in A are for a 5-V supply, although any supply up to about 25 V can be protected by simply choosing the appropriate zener diode. When the supply voltage exceeds the zener voltage (+0.7 V), the transistor turns on and fires the thyristor. This shorts out the supply, and prevents the voltage rising any further. In the case of a supply with only fuse protection, it is better to connect the thyristor to the regulator circuit when the crowbar operates. The thyristor should have a current rating about twice the expected short-circuit current and a maximum voltage greater than the supply voltage. The circuit can be reset by either switching off the supply or by breaking the thyristor circuit with a switch.

FAST-ACTING POWER-SUPPLY PROTECTION

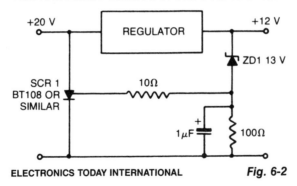

ELECTRONICS TODAY INTERNATIONAL

Fig. 6-2

When using a regulated power supply to reduce a supply voltage, there is always the danger that component failure in the power supply might lead to a severe overvoltage condition across the load. To cope with overvoltage situations, the circuit is designed to protect the load during overvoltage conditions. Component values given are for a 20-V supply with regulated output at 12 V. The zener diode can be changed according to whatever voltage is to be the maximum. If the voltage at the regulator output rises to 13 V or higher, the zener diode breaks down and triggers the thyristor, which shorts out the supply line and blows the main fuse.

5-V CROWBAR

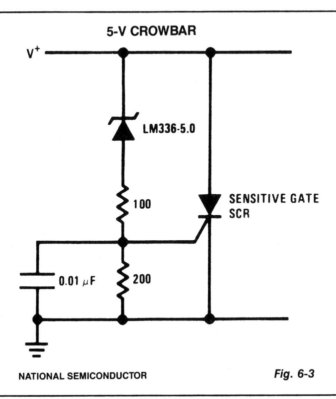

NATIONAL SEMICONDUCTOR

Fig. 6-3

OVERVOLTAGE PROTECTION WITH AUTOMATIC RESET

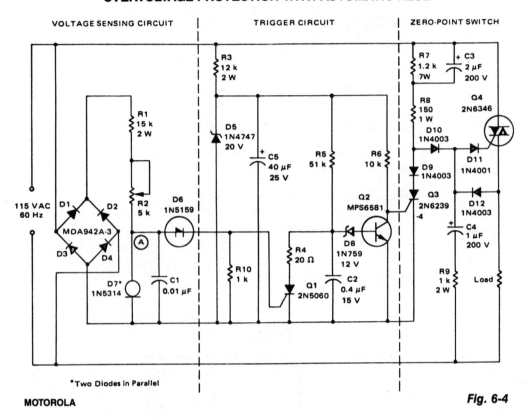

VOLTAGE SENSING CIRCUIT | TRIGGER CIRCUIT | ZERO-POINT SWITCH

*Two Diodes in Parallel

MOTOROLA

Fig. 6-4

OVERVOLTAGE PROTECTION FOR LOGIC

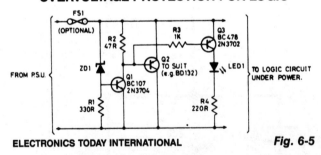

ELECTRONICS TODAY INTERNATIONAL

Fig. 6-5

Zener diode ZD1 senses the supply, and should the supply rise above 6 V, Q1 will turn on. In turn, Q2 conducts clamping the rail. Subsequent events depend on the source supply. It will either shut down, go into current limit, or blow its supply fuse. None of these will damage the TTL chips. The rating of Q2 depends on the source supply, and whether it will be required to operate continuously in the event of failure. Its current rating has to be in excess of the source supply.

OVERVOLTAGE PROTECTION CIRCUIT (SCR CROWBAR)

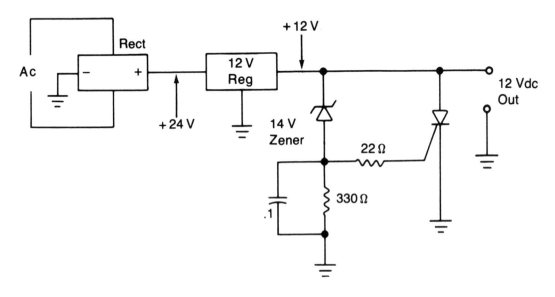

WILLIAM SHEETS

Fig. 6-6

The silicon-controlled rectifier (SCR) is rated to handle at least the current of the power supply. It is connected in parallel across the 12-Vdc output lines, but remains inert until a voltage appears at the gate terminal. This triggering voltage is supplied by the zener diode. At potentials less than 14 V, the zener will not conduct current. But, at potentials greater than 14 Vdc, the zener conducts and creates a voltage drop across the 330-Ω resistor that will fire the SCR. When the SCR turns on, the output lines of the power supply are shorted to ground. This will blow the primary fuse or burn out the transformer if there is no primary fuse.

POWER-SUPPLY PROTECTION CIRCUIT

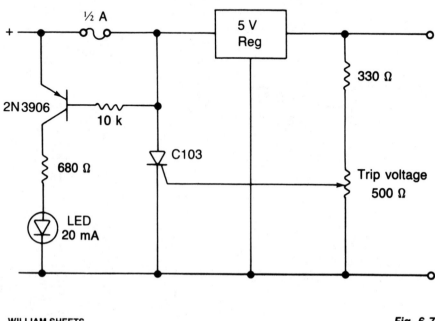

WILLIAM SHEETS

Fig. 6-7

When using a regulated supply to reduce a supply voltage there is always the danger of component failure in the supply and consequent damage to the equipment. A fuse will protect when excess current is drawn, but might be too slow to cope with overvoltage conditions. The values shown are for a 12-V supply being dropped to 5 V. The trip voltage is set to 5.7 V to protect the equipment in the event of a regulator fault. The 330-Ω resistor and the 500-Ω potentiometer form a potential divider, which samples the output voltage as set by adjustment of the potentiometer. The SCR is selected to carry at least twice the fuse rating. The full supply voltage is connected to the input of the regulator. The 2N2906 is held bias off by the 10-kΩ resistor and the SCR so that the LED is held off. If the output voltage rises above a set trip value, the SCR will conduct, the fuse will blow, the 2N3906 will be supplied with base current via the 10-kΩ resistor, and the LED will light up.

Sources

Chapter 1

Fig. 1-1. Reprinted from EDN, 7/21/88, © 1989 Cahners Publishing Co., a division of Reed Publishing USA.

Fig. 1-2. Reprinted with permission of National Semiconductor Corp., Voltage Regulator Handbook, p. 7-32.

Fig. 1-3. Ham Radio, 12/79, p. 67.

Fig. 1-4. 73 Amateur Radio, 2/83, p. 99.

Fig. 1-5. Siliconix, MOSpower Applications Handbook, p. 6-176.

Fig. 1-6. Reprinted with permission of National Semiconductor Corp., Linear Databook, 1982, p. 9-31.

Fig. 1-7. Reprinted with permission of National Semiconductor Corp., Voltage Regulator Handbook, p. 10-141.

Fig. 1-8. Electronics Today International, 11/80.

Fig. 1-9. 73 Amateur Radio, 7/77.

Fig. 1-10. 73 Amateur Radio, 2/79, p. 156.

Fig. 1-11. 73 Amateur Radio, 7/77.

Fig. 1-12. Reprinted with permission from GE Semiconductor Department. GE SCR Manual, Sixth Edition, 1979, p. 203.

Fig. 1-13. Courtesy of Motorola Inc., Application Note AN-294, p.6.

Fig. 1-14. Texas Instruments, Linear and Interface Circuits Applications, Vol. 1, p. 6-24.

Fig. 1-15. Popular Electronics, 7/89, p. 81.

Fig. 1-16. Linear Technology Corp., Linear Databook, 1986, p. 4-15.

Fig. 1-17. Radio-Electronics, 7/86, p. 67.

Fig. 1-18. Motorola, Motorola Thyristor Device Data, Series A 1985, p. 1-6-46.

Fig. 1-19. 44 Electronics Projects for SWLs, BDers, and Radio Experimenters, TAB Book No. 1258, p. 153.

Fig. 1-20. Yuasa Battery (America) Inc., Application Manual for NP Type Battery.

Fig. 1-21. Intersil, Component Data Catalog, 1987, p. 2-108.

Fig. 1-22. Electronic Design, 7/76, p. 120.

Fig. 1-23. Courtesy William Sheets.

Fig. 1-24. Linear Technology Corp., Linear Applications Handbook, 1987, p. AN6-3.

Fig. 1-25. Courtesy William Sheets.

Fig. 1-26. Motorola, Motorola Thyristor Device Data, Series A 1985, p. 1-6-54.

Fig. 1-27. ZeTeX (formerly Ferranti), Technical Handbook Super E-Line Transistors, 1987, p. SE-164.

Fig. 1-28. Moli Energy Limited.

Fig. 1-29. CQ, 7/82, p. 18.

Fig. 1-30. Motorola, TMOS Power FET Design Ideas, 1985, p. 8.

Fig. 1-31. Linear Technology Corp., Linear Databook Supplement, 1988, p. S5-11.

Chapter 2

Fig. 2-1. Texas Instruments, Linear and Interface Circuits Applications, 1985, Vol. 1, p. 6-34.

Fig. 2-2. Reprinted from EDN, 5/5/78, © 1989 Cahners Publishing Co., a division of Reed Publishing USA.

Fig. 2-3. Hands-On Electronics, 7-8/86.

Fig. 2-4. Harris, Analog Product Data Book, 1988, p. 10-107.

Fig. 2-5. GE/RCA, BiMOS Operational Amplifiers Circuit Ideas, 1987, p. 12.

Fig. 2-6. 73 Amateur Radio, 4/88, p. 20.

Fig. 2-7. Reprinted from EDN, 12/8/88, © 1989 Cahners Publishing Co., a division of Reed Publishing USA.

Fig. 2-8. Linear Technology Corp., Linear Applications Handbook, 1987, p. AN8-4.

Fig. 2-9. Ham Radio, 7/89, p.20.

Fig. 2-10. GE, Optoelectronics, Third Edition, Ch. 6, p. 152.

Fig. 2-11. Siliconix, MOSpower Applications Handbook, p. 6-62.

Fig. 2-12. Texas Instruments, Linear and Interface Circuits Applications, 1987, p. 12-5.

Fig. 2-13. Maxim, 1986 Power Supply Circuits, p. 27.

Fig. 2-14. Texas Instruments, Linear and Interface Circuits Applications, 1985, Vol. 1, p. 6-36.

Fig. 2-15. Texas Instruments, Linear and Interface Circuits Applications, 1985, Vol. 1, p. 6-36.

Fig. 2-16. QST, 6/88, p. 48.

Fig. 2-17. Texas Instruments, Linear Circuits Data Book, 1989, p. 2-74.

Fig. 2-18. Hands-On Electronics, Fact Card No. 49.

Fig. 2-19. Popular Electronics, Fact Card No. 100.

Fig. 2-20. Linear Technology Corp., Linear Applications Handbook, 1987, p. AN3-13.

Fig. 2-21. 73 Amateur Radio, 5/88, p. 90.

Fig. 2-22. Reprinted from EDN, 7/7/88, © 1989 Cahners Publishing Co., a division of Reed Publishing USA.

Fig. 2-23. Harris, Analog Product Data Book, 1988, p. 10-16.

Fig. 2-24. Reprinted with permission from Electronic Design, © 1988, Penton Publishing.

Fig. 2-25. Maxim, Seminar Applications Book, 1988/89, p. 83.

Fig. 2-26. Intersil, Applications Handbook, 1988, p. 6-18.

Fig. 2-27. Popular Electronics, Fact Card No. 100.

Fig. 2-28. Popular Electronics, Fact Card No. 95.

Fig. 2-29. Motorola, Motorola TMOS Power FET Design Ideas, 1985, p. 38.

Fig. 2-30. 73 Amateur Radio, 6/89. p. 61.

Fig. 2-31. Electronic Engineering, 2/87, p. 44.

Fig. 2-32. Popular Electronics, Fact Card No. 100.

Fig. 2-33. Intersil, Applications Handbook, 1988, p. 6-70.

Fig. 2-34. Intersil, Applications Handbook, 1988, p. 6-17.

Fig. 2-35. Motorola, Motorola TMOS Power FET Design Ideas, 1985, p. 14.

Fig. 2-36. Electronics Today International, 6/77, p. 77.

Fig. 2-37. Courtesy of Motorola Inc., Linear Integrated Circuits, 1979, p. 4-15.

Fig. 2-38. Courtesy of Motorola Inc., Linear Integrated Circuits, 1979, p. 4-15.

Fig. 2-39. Radio-Electronics, 6/86, p. 52.

Fig. 2-40. Courtesy William Sheets.

Fig. 2-41. GE/RCA, BiMOS Operational Amplifiers Circuit Ideas, 1987, p. 24.

Fig. 2-42. Texas Instruments, Linear and Interface Circuits Applications, Vol. 1, 1985, p. 6-35.

Fig. 2-43. Electronics Today International, 3/75, p. 67.

Fig. 2-44. Reprinted with the permission of National Semiconductor Corp., Voltage Regulator Handbook, p. 10-179.

Fig. 2-45. Linear Technology Corp., Linear Applications Handbook, 1987, p. AN3-15.

Fig. 2-46. © Siliconix Inc., MOSpower Design Catalog, 1/83, p. 6-71.

Fig. 2-47. ZeTeX (formerly Ferranti Semiconductors), Technical Handbook, Vol. 10, Data Converters, 1983, p. 3-12.

Fig. 2-48. Courtesy of Motorola Inc., Linear Integrated Circuits, 1979, p. 5-144.

Fig. 2-49. Intersil, Intersil Data Book, 5/83, p. 5-201.

Fig. 2-50. Signetics, Signetics 555 Timers, 1973, p. 27.

Fig. 2-51. Signetics, Signetics Analog Data Manual, 1982, p. 6-21.

Fig. 2-52. Signetics, Signetics Analog Data Manual, 1982, p. 12-36.

Fig. 2-53. Signetics, Signetics Analog Data Manual, 1982, p. 12-26.

Fig. 2-54. Popular Electronics, Fact Card No. 100.

Fig. 2-55. Popular Electronics, Fact Card No. 95.

Fig. 2-56. Maxim, 1986 Power Supply Circuits, p. 26.

Fig. 2-57. Electronic Engineering, 1/87, p. 22.

Fig. 2-58. Electronic Engineering, 12/84, p. 41.

Fig. 2-59. Courtesy of Motorola, TMOS Power FET Design Ideas, 1985, p. 43.

Fig. 2-60. Motorola, Thyristor Device Data, Series A, 1985, p. 1-6-55.

Fig. 2-61. Siliconix, MOSpower Applications Handbook, p. 6-51.

Fig. 2-62. GE/RCA, BiMOS Operational Amplifiers Circuit Ideas, 1987, p. 24.

Fig. 2-63. Signetics, Signetics Analog Data Manual, 1983, p.12-22.

Fig. 2-64. Electronics Today International, 7/75, p. 39.

Fig. 2-65. Signetics, Signetics Analog Data Manual, 1982, p. 6-14.

Fig. 2-66. Courtesy of Motorola Inc., Linear Integrated Circuits, 1979, p. 3-147.

Fig. 2-67. Electronics Today International, 3/75, p. 67.

Fig. 2-68. Courtesy of Motorola, Linear Integrated Circuits, 1979,p. 4-50.

Fig. 2-69. 73 Amateur Radio, 3/77, p. 152.

Fig. 2-70. Intersil, Intersil Data Book, 5/83, p. 5-77.

Fig. 2-71. Intersil, Intersil Data Book, 5/83, p. 5-77.

Fig. 2-72. Intersil, Intersil Data Book, 5/83, p. 5-77.

Fig. 2-73. Intersil, Intersil Data Book, 5/83, p. 5-77.

Fig. 2-74. Intersil, Intersil Data Book, 5/83, p. 5-76.

Fig. 2-75. Courtesy of Motorola Inc., Linear Integrated Circuits, 1979, p. 4-105.

Fig. 2-76. Reprinted with the permission of National Semiconductor Corp., Voltage Regulator Handbook, p. 10-15.

Fig. 2-77. Reprinted with the permission of National Semiconductor Corp., Voltage Regulator Handbook, p. 10-77.

Fig. 2-78. Courtesy of Motorola Inc., Linear Integrated Circuits, 1979, p. 4-105.

Fig. 2-79. Courtesy of Motorola Inc., Linear Integrated Circuits, 1979, p. 4-105.

Fig. 2-80. Electronics Today International, 1/70, p. 45.

Fig. 2-81. Motorola, Linear Integrated Circuits, p. 3-138.

Fig. 2-82. Electronic Design, 11/29/84, p. 282.

Fig. 2-83. 73 Amateur Radio, 12/70, p. 170.

Fig. 2-84. Signetics, Analog Data Manual, 1983, p. 12-27.

Fig. 2-85. Electronic Engineering, 1/85, p. 45.

Fig. 2-86. Signetics, 1987 Linear Data Manual, Vol. 2: Industrial, 2/87, p. 8-223.

Fig. 2-87. Siliconix, MOSpower Applications Handbook, p. 6-59.

Fig. 2-88. Linear Technology Corp., Linear Databook, 1986, p. 3-23.

Fig. 2-89. Electronic Engineering, 10/84, p. 38.

Fig. 2-90. NASA, NASA Tech Briefs, Summer 1985, p. 32.

Fig. 2-91. NASA, NASA Tech Briefs, 9/87, p. 21.

Fig. 2-92. Signetics, Signetics Analog Data Manual, 1983, p. 12-28.

Fig. 2-93. Motorola, TMOS Power FET Design Ideas, 1985, p. 37.

Fig. 2-94. Reprinted from EDN, 10/1/87, © 1989 Cahners Publishing Co., a division of Reed Publishing USA.

Fig. 2-95. Texas Instruments, Linear and Interface Circuit Applications, 1985, p. 7-19.

Fig. 2-96. Linear Technology, 1986 Linear Databook, p. 3-22.

Fig. 2-97. Courtesy of Motorola Inc., Circuit Applications for the Triac, AN-466, p. 12.

Chapter 3

Fig. 3-1. Electronic Engineering, 10/76, p.17.

Fig. 3-2. Electronic Engineering, 7/77, p. 26.

Fig. 3-3. Popular Electronics, 5/74, p. 24.

Fig. 3-4. NASA, NASA Tech Briefs, 1/88, p. 22.

Fig. 3-5. Reprinted from EDN, 6/22/89, © 1989 Cahners Publishing Co., a division of Reed Publishing USA.

Fig. 3-6. Motorola, TMOS Power FET Design Ideas, 1985, p. 40.

Fig. 3-7. Popular Electronics, 10/89, p. 37.

Fig. 3-8. Hands-On Electronics, 12/86, p. 93.

Fig. 3-9. Electronic Engineering, Applied Ideas, 3/86, p. 33.

Fig. 3-10. Reprinted from EDN, 9/15/82 and 1/6/83, © 1989 Cahners Publishing Co., a division of Reed Publishing USA.

Fig. 3-11. Reprinted from EDN, 10/17/85, © 1989 Cahners Publishing Co., a division of Reed Publishing USA.

Fig. 3-12. Linear Technology Corp., Linear Applications Handbook, 1987, p. AN2-7.

Fig. 3-13. Hands-On Electronics, 12/86, p.92.

Fig. 3-14. NASA, NASA Tech Briefs, Summer 1985, p. 48.

Fig. 3-15. Reprinted from EDN, 4/20/77, © 1989 Cahners Publishing Co., a division of Reed Publishing USA.

Fig. 3-16. Siliconix, MOSpower Applications Handbook, p. 6-59.

Fig. 3-17. Motorola, TMOS Power FET Design Ideas, 1985, p. 42.

Fig. 3-18. Gernsback Publications Inc., 42 New Ideas, 1984, p. 18.

Fig. 3-19. Popular Electronics, 8/89 p. 29.

Fig. 3-20. Courtesy William Sheets.

Chapter 4

Fig. 4-1. Reprinted with permission of National Semiconductor Corp., Linear Databook, 1982, p. 1-68.

Fig. 4-2. Signetics, Signetics Analog Data Manual, 1982, p. 6-25.

Fig. 4-3. Signetics, Signetics Analog Data Manual, 1982, p. 6-25.

Fig. 4-4. Siliconix, MOSpower Applications Handbook, p. 6-62.

Fig. 4-5. Courtesy of Motorola Inc., Linear Integrated Circuits, 1979, p. 4-15.

Fig. 4-6. Reprinted with the permission of National Semiconductor Corp., CMOS Databook, 1981, p. 6-38.

Fig. 4-7. Electronics Today International, 4/82, p. 29.

Fig. 4-8. Reprinted with the permission of National Semiconductor Corp., Voltage Regulator Handbook, p. 10-142.

Fig. 4-9. Signetics, Analog Data Manual, 1982, p. 6-25.

Fig. 4-10. Reprinted with the permission of National Semiconductor Corp., Voltage Regulator Handbook, p. 10-77.

Fig. 4-11. Reprinted with the permission of National Semiconductor Corp., Voltage Regulator Handbook, p. 10-15.

Fig. 4-12. Reprinted with the permission of National Semiconductor Corp., Linear Databook, 1982, p. 1-68.

Fig. 4-13. Electronics Today International, 1/75, p. 67.

Fig. 4-14. Reprinted with the permission of National Semiconductor Corp., Voltage Regulator Handbook, p. 10-15.

Fig. 4-15. Reprinted with the permission of National Semiconductor Corp., Linear Databook, 1982, p. 2-8.

Fig. 4-16. Courtesy of Motorola Inc., Linear Integrated Circuits, 1979, p. 4-23.

Fig. 4-17. Electronics Today International, 8/78, p. 91.

Fig. 4-18. Courtesy of Motorola Inc., Linear Integrated Circuits, 1979, p. 4-15.

Fig. 4-19. Electronics Today International, 9/75, p. 64.

Fig. 4-20. Electronics Today International, 3/75, p. 68.

Fig. 4-21. Electronics Today International, 1/75, p. 67.

Fig. 4-22. Courtesy of Motorola Inc., Linear Integrated Circuits, 1979, p. 4-152.

Chapter 5

Fig. 5-1. NASA, NASA Tech Briefs, Winter 1985, p. 52.

Fig. 5-2. Electronic Engineering, 3/86, p. 34.

Fig. 5-3. Courtesy William Sheets.

Fig. 5-4. Hands-On Electronics, 1-2/86, p. 96.

Fig. 5-5. Maxim, 1986 Power Supply Circuits, p. 120.

Chapter 6

Fig. 6-1. Electronics Today International, 3/77, p. 71.

Fig. 6-2. Electronics Today International, 8/76, p. 66.

Fig. 6-3. Reprinted with the permission of National Semiconductor Corp., Linear Databook, 1982, p. 2-39.

Fig. 6-4. Courtesy of Motorola Inc., Circuit Applications for the Triac, AN-466, p. 14.

Fig. 6-5. Electronics Today International, 1/79, p. 95.

Fig. 6-6. Courtesy William Sheets.

Fig. 6-7. Courtesy William Sheets.

Index

W

Z

Other Bestsellers of Related Interest

ENCYCLOPEDIA OF ELECTRONIC CIRCUITS
Vol. 1—Rudolf F. Graf

". . . schematics that encompass virtually the entire spectrum of electronics technology . . . This is a well worthwhile book to have handy."

—***Modern Electronics***

Discover hundreds of the most versatile electronic and integrated circuit designs, all available at the turn of a page. You'll find circuit diagrams and schematics for a wide variety of practical applications. Many entries also include clear, concise explanations of the circuit configurations and functions. 768 pages, 1,762 illustrations. Book No. 1938, $29.95 paperback, $60.00 hardcover

THE COMPLETE BOOK OF OSCILLOSCOPES
—2nd Edition—Stan Prentiss

Save hours of troubleshooting time by mastering top-of-the-line scopes with the professional advice in this book. It reviews the oscilloscope equipment and advanced testing procedures developed during the last five years. You'll appreciate this book's easy-to-read style, logical format, and original photographs taken by video communications expert Stan Prentiss in his electronics laboratory. 320 pages, 165 illustrations. Book No. 3825, $16.95 paperback, $26.95 hardcover

UNDERSTANDING ELECTRONICS—3rd Edition
—R.H. Warring, Edited by G. Randy Slone

Revised with state-of-the-art information on all the modern advances in electronics, this classic sourcebook is more complete than ever! You'll find thorough coverage of all the basics of electronics, and everything from ac and dc power to the developing new fields of photoelectronics and digital computing. This book offers all the information you need to begin designing and building your own circuits. 230 pages, 188 illustrations. Book No. 3044, $12.95 paperback only

THE ILLUSTRATED DICTIONARY OF ELECTRONICS—5th Edition
—Rufus P. Turner and Stan Gibilisco

This completely revised and updated edition defines more than 27,000 practical electronics terms, acronyms, and abbreviations. Find up-to-date information on basic electronics, computers, mathematics, electricity, communications, and state-of-the-art applications—all discussed in a nontechnical style. The author also includes 360 new definitions and 125 illustrations and diagrams. 736 pages, 650 illustrations. Book No. 3345, $26.95 paperback, $39.95 hardcover

POWER SUPPLIES: Switching Regulators, Inverters & Converters—Irving M. Gottlieb

Understanding how power sources operate in everything from computers and radio transmitters to TVs, and more! This book contains the details and depth required by electronics professionals and the basic explanations and advice needed by hobbyists. It offers a wide range of related technical data in a single format. 448 pages, 260 illustrations. Book 1665, $21.95 paperback only

ELECTRONIC POWER CONTROL: Circuits, Devices & Techniques—Irving M. Gottlieb

This guide focuses on the specific digital circuits used in electronic power applications. It presents state-of-the-art approaches to analysis, troubleshooting, and implementation of new solid-state devices. Gottlieb shows you how to adapt various power-control techniques to your individual needs. He uses descriptive analysis and real-world applications wherever possible, employing mathematical theory only when relevant. 272 pages, 197 illustrations. Book No. 3837, $17.95 paperback, $27.95 hardcover

THE MODERN OSCILLATOR CIRCUIT ENCYCLOPEDIA—Rudolf F. Graf

An outstanding collection of easy-to-apply oscillator circuits.

This valuable reference contains an assortment of more than 250 ready-to-use oscillator circuit designs that represent the latest engineering practices. Rudolf F. Graf covers the whole spectrum of audio-to-UHF frequency oscillator circuits with various configurations and output characteristics.

Each entry includes a schematic, a brief explanation of how the circuit works, and the original source of the circuit for readers who want additional information. 192 pages, 300 illustrations. Book No. 3893, $12.95 paperback only

ENCYCLOPEDIA OF ELECTRONIC CIRCUITS— Vol. 4—Rudolf F. Graf and William Sheets

"You'll love this book if you find pleasure from building circuits . . . definitely a book for the workshop library."

—**Practical Electronics**

This fourth volume includes schematics and descriptions for the latest circuitry used in computers, controls, instrumentation, telecommunications, sensors, and numerous other electronics applications. This monumental work features more than 1,000 all-new circuits in 100 alphabetically-arranged categories. Clear, comprehensive, and meticulously organized, this is by far the best source of modern circuit designs for hobbyists and professionals. 768 pages, 1000 illustrations. Book No. 3752, $29.95 paperback, $60.00 hardcover

Prices Subject to Change Without Notice.

Look for These and Other TAB Books at Your Local Bookstore

To Order Call Toll Free 1-800-822-8158

(in PA, AK, and Canada call 717-794-2191)

or write to TAB Books, Blue Ridge Summit, PA 17294-0840.

Title		Product No.	Quantity	Price

☐ Check or money order made payable to TAB Books

Charge my ☐ VISA ☐ MasterCard ☐ American Express

Acct. No. _____ Exp. _____

Signature: _____

Name: _____

Address: _____

City: _____

State: _____ Zip: _____

Subtotal $ _____

Postage and Handling
($3.00 in U.S., $5.00 outside U.S.) $ _____

Add applicable state and local
sales tax $ _____

TOTAL $ _____

TAB Books catalog free with purchase; otherwise send $1.00 in check or money order and receive a $1.00 credit on your next purchase.

Orders outside U.S. must pay with international money order in U.S. dollars.

TAB Guarantee: If for any reason you are not satisfied with the book(s) you order, simply return it (them) within 15 days and receive a full refund. **BC**